"Happy Birtday"
Dear Edit,
Tonight
It's might interest you
love
Maureen

HONEY AND YOUR HEALTH
by Bodog F. Beck and Dorée Smedley

is a standard work on a most fascinating subject: the story of honey—nature's "miracle" health food—and its present-day importance as a staple in your daily diet.

HONEY AND YOUR HEALTH

includes all the facts that science has discovered about the virtues and uses of honey. Honey used as a remedy in sickness. The place of honey in the science of modern nutrition. Honey as a natural sweet—its superiority to sugar.

HONEY AND YOUR HEALTH

tempts the palate with a recipe section listing myriad golden goodies made possible with honey.

HONEY
AND
YOUR HEALTH
A NUTRIMENTAL, MEDICINAL
AND HISTORICAL COMMENTARY

By
BODOG F. BECK, M.D.
and
DORÉE SMEDLEY

"My son, eat thou honey, for it is good."—Solomon
(Proverbs 24:13)

A NATIONAL GENERAL COMPANY

HONEY AND YOUR HEALTH

*A Bantam Book / published by arrangement with
Dodd, Mead & Company*

PRINTING HISTORY

Robert McBride edition published April 1938 as
Honey and Health, *Copyright, 1938, by Bodog F. Beck.*
New revised edition published 1944
Dodd, Mead edition published 1948
Seven printings through 1965
Bantam edition published May 1971

PREFACE TO ORIGINAL EDITION

The principal aim and object of this volume is to evaluate honey and appraise its true worth, particularly as an important nutrimental and superior medicinal substance. The author's venture in preparing and publishing this review during moments snatched from the hubbub of an active medical practice was inspired by a long cherished ambition to contribute his best efforts to the reinstatement of honey to its former exalted place. The advantages and efficacy of this substance should be appreciated.

For someone who knows the extraordinary merits of honey, it is difficult to comprehend the reason why this salutary substance has suffered such a setback. For sixty centuries, throughout historic ages and undoubtedly even in prehistoric times, honey was man's only "sweetener" and his most favored food, delicacy and medicine. But Nature's own sweet was displaced by one of man's inferior, nay, objectionable products. Upon the intrusion of "refined" sugars, honey declined in use and now, instead of being an important household necessity, it has become an article of luxury. Civilization and even science often post only dim lights as warning signals before deep chasms; on the other hand, they neglect to mark with road-signs abandoned paths which lead to a better life.

The culpable disregard of honey is a grave and lamentable error of the present generation and a sad reflection on its intelligence. It is almost unbelievable that such an ideal and nourishing food, with its delightful bouquet, is almost entirely missing from our tables. If honey were ever rehabilitated, man would wonder how he could ever have gotten along without it.

The medicinal merits of honey are fully discussed in the

respective chapters of this book. The author considers it an especial privilege to avail himself of an opportunity at least to try to promote the physical, and indirectly, the moral welfare of his fellowmen. It accords a sense of gratification to hope that the advocated measures may benefit society.

It is curious that the numberless books on dietetics scarcely mention or only superficially treat the subject of honey. This applies to lay as well as to medical literature. While the ancient classical writers and those of the Middle Ages liberally contributed to the practical knowledge and appreciation of honey, their extravagant statements today sound fantastic, almost absurd. Their faith in the substance was so implicit that the information one gains from their comments has the aspect of legendary lore rather than of facts. On the other hand, the disregard of honey in current literature is diametrically opposite. It is astounding how meager are the scientific data available today concerning honey. Not a single book has been published of late years which creditably and thoroughly discusses its nutrimental and medicinal values. This actuality was an additional incentive for editing the present volume. May it induce further research in this almost virgin field.

B. F. B.

New York City
January, 1938

CONTENTS

PART I—HONEY AND YOUR HEALTH

PART II—THE HISTORY OF HONEY

ACKNOWLEDGMENTS

Thanks are extended to Mr. E. R. Root, senior editor of *Gleanings in Bee Culture*, Medina, Ohio; Dr. E. F. Phillips, Professor of Apiculture, Cornell University, Ithaca, N. Y.; Mr. Robert B. Willson, vice-president of the John G. Paton Company; and Mr. Francis H. Mattutat, of the John G. Paton Company, for their generous assistance and co-operation. Their helpful suggestions and contributions of factual material greatly aided the research necessary for this book.

Thanks are due also to Miss Harriet M. Grace, Director of the American Honey Institute, Madison, Wis., for her permission to use certain honey recipes developed by the American Honey Institute, and Miss Sally Larkin, editor of *American Cookery*, for the delightful recipes she contributed; also the Golden Blossom Test Kitchen, for the many interesting new honey recipes appearing in this book.

INTRODUCTION

Through my friendship for the author, it has been my privilege to read the manuscript of this book. Thus I have been given an opportunity to have a brief word with others who will read the book after publication.

First I wish to congratulate the readers on obtaining such a vast store of information on the merits of honey and the wonders of its past recognition. In the rush of modern affairs we are prone to overlook old beliefs and traditions and to forget that they ever existed. While today we do not concede that honey cures all human ailments, it is nevertheless interesting to learn that earlier people held such views. The lore which the author has so well collected, not only on bees but also on honey, is, however, far greater than could possibly be included in a single book. With such an array of expressions of faith in honey, we are perforce brought to increase our own confidence in this worthy product.

Honey has needed just such a book as this. Modern works on honey have dealt chiefly with its chemistry and physics, with some attention to its dietetic value and more to its use in cookery. These are rather prosaic aspects of an interesting and delectable article of human diet, by no means to be scorned, but on the other hand not to be pursued to the exclusion of the romantic side. It is not surprising that bee-keepers attribute almost supernatural virtues to a substance which they assist the bees to produce but there is no impropriety on the part of others, not so engaged, if they question the merits claimed by enthusiasts. Statements which this book contains should give pause to everyone who disdains the opinions of those without scientific attainments. I have no intention to belittle scientific investigations but there is, on the other hand, something to be said for accumulated experience.

I am happy to commend this work to the general public, to the beekeepers and, last but not least, to the medical profession. I sincerely hope that it may serve the purpose for which it is intended.

E. F. PHILLIPS

Cornell University
Ithaca, New York, 1938

PART I

HONEY AND YOUR HEALTH

CHAPTER I

HONEY—THE YOUTH ELIXIR OF ANTIQUITY

If you were to sit down to breakfast one morning to find an Egyptian charm of 10,000 years ago beside your plate, you would probably be quite startled and amused. Yet, the jar of honey that appears on the breakfast table of so many homes has a history considerably older than the oldest Egyptian relic ever unearthed. It is one of the rare links between our modern world and prehistoric ages. The earliest man used honey for his breakfast long before he quit roaming the forests and settled down in peaceful valleys where he learned to grow his food, domesticate animals and evolve a language. He gathered wild honey from the virgin forests to eke out his diet. In fact, he learned to use honey as a food before he learned to eat bread, milk or cereals. It is one of the oldest foods known to man, and perhaps the most romantic.

THE ANCIENTS REGARDED HONEY AS A SACRED SUBSTANCE

The sacrifices made to the pagan gods of the early primitive societies always included vessels of aromatic honey. Men assumed that the gods found honey as indispensable to their happiness as did they themselves. The tomb of an Egyptian king was not complete without lotus blossoms, jars of fragrant honey and boxes of honey cakes. The walls of his final resting place were decorated with scenes depicting the life of the

3

Egyptian beekeeper, and showed the beekeeper at work gathering honey, and removing the combs from the hives with the aid of smoke, straining honey into great jars and sealing these jars. Honey was regarded as a sacred substance, the purest and best thing in this imperfect world—a symbol of eternal bliss.

The religious rites of the ancient Assyrians, Babylonians, Chaldeans, Phœnicians and Hebrews included the use of honey in all ceremonies. These people very much doubted man's ability to go to Heaven without a vessel of honey at his side—or that he would find very much happiness on earth unless bestowed with a jar of honey at his birth. All of the important events of a man's life were consecrated by religious ceremonies in which honey was used in the rituals to symbolize purity and goodness.

Every marriage contract in ancient Egypt required the bridegroom to promise to supply his bride every year of their married life with a certain amount of honey. When the nuptial knot was tied, the bridegroom would say, "I take you for my wife and bind myself to furnish you annually with twenty-four hins [thirty-two pounds] of honey." Thus he promised to love and cherish her always. The early Hindu wedding ceremonies in India were more elaborate. Honey was served to each of the guests. Then the bridegroom would kiss the bride and say, "This is honey, the speech of my tongue is honey, and the honey of the bee is dwelling in my mouth." During the ceremony the bride's forehead, lips, eyelids and ear lobes were anointed with honey. In Bengal, the Brahmans followed a similar ritual. It was believed that the great purity of honey would ward off evil spirits during the marriage celebration and thereby insure the pair long years of happiness and bliss.

LOVE STIMULANTS

With the passage of time, new and colorful theories sprang up about honey as an elixir of love. The older societies clung to their faith in honey as a pure and magical substance, and continued to use it in their religious ceremonies and also to rely on it as an important part of their daily diet. But in other parts of the Old World honey came to be known as an aphrodisiac. Many contrary ideas and beliefs about an identical food existed side by side in the early civilizations. The great distances between the communities, the difficulties inherent in travel, and the barriers of language made this inevitable.

Many of the Asiatic peoples regarded honey as a magical substance that controlled the fertility of women, the cattle, and also the crops. Some of the Mediterranean tribes believed that the use of honey in their religious rites prevented blight and pestilence from overtaking their land. Others, like the Moors, frankly regarded honey as a love stimulant. In Morocco, a wedding celebration was a sex orgy. The guests were served honey and honey wines until they became intoxicated. After the wedding ceremony had been concluded, the bridegroom was expected to retire from the gathering to his own quarters and feast upon honey, for the Moroccans believed that honey had a powerful aphrodisiac effect.

On the European continent honey became an important ingredient in all ancient satyriaca (*ad coitum tentaginem irritantia facientia*). In fact, for centuries nearly all of the love elixirs and philters of both the East and the West have been made principally with honey.

From the medical standpoint, there is no basis for the assumption that honey is an aphrodisiac. But it is easy to understand why this idea would gain credence among an ignorant and half-starved people. Honey is rapidly assimilated and is an excellent source of quick energy. An anemic, poorly nourished individual who was given an elixir made with honey would probably experience a sudden glow of well-being and renewed energy directly after taking it. There is nothing mysterious about this. Any half-starved creature who was given an easily assimilated food or beverage on an empty stomach would experience the same sensation. Otherwise, the power of honey as a love stimulant would depend wholly upon the individual's imagination.

THE GREEKS HAD A THEORY FOR IT

The ancient Greeks evolved their own ideas about the value of honey as a food. They apparently chose to ignore the Eastern rationalizations about honey as an aphrodisiac. Whether they knew the truth about it or merely found this legend embarrassing is hard to say. Athenian culture of the fifth century B.C. placed a strong emphasis on the suppression of sex. The Greeks did not consider sex activities immoral but inconvenient. They argued that an interest in sex interfered with the intellectual life, took up too much time, caused too many perturbations of the spirit and was generally a nuisance. So they frowned upon it.

This national ban on love had a number of interesting consequences. The "platonic" relationship was invented. The "intellectual soul mate" made her appearance in society. The home was relegated to a place in the country where a respectable Greek might keep a wife and family in decent obscurity. He might even visit them once a year or so. But if he was an Athenian in good standing, he lived apart from them and dedicated his talents to intellectual pursuits, to athletics and the quest for physical perfection, to intellectual debates and to the task of improving the intellectual standards of his platonic soul mate. Obviously, honey as an aphrodisiac would have thrown a monkey wrench into this intellectual atmosphere. Most Greeks were fond of honey and consumed a great deal of it every day. They assured each other that it was a youth elixir.

The philosophers and mathematicians of Athens were probably responsible for the theory that honey was an important food substance for prolonging youth. Quite a number of them experimented with honey diets. They were convinced that a man's life span could be almost doubled if he were to discover exactly the right foods for his physical needs. They believed that honey was one of the essential foods for such a plan. The Greek athletes were always given honey and water to drink after the Olympic games. It was found that this mixture quickly banished fatigue. The philosophers wondered whether honey might not be used to banish fatigue altogether. If one never grew tired, perhaps one might never grow old.

Pythagoras, the Greek philosopher (and the first man to conceive of the earth as a globe self-supported in space and revolving with other planets around a central luminary), gave a great deal of thought to this matter. He finally adopted a diet that included a generous amount of honey and bread. The members of the Pythagorean School followed his example. Other scholars in Athens experimented with honey diets of their own. One of the most popular was honey and milk— a mixture that became best known in Athenian circles as "ambrosia."

The all-liquid diets proved to be unsound and were soon

abandoned. But the diet that Pythagoras planned for himself and his followers, which included fruits, nuts and vegetables as well as honey and bread, brought about an immense improvement in his vigor and health. His followers also enjoyed a new energy and youthfulness. Pythagoras lived to be ninety. One of his disciples, Appolonius, lived to be one hundred and thirteen years of age. Anacreon, who died at the age of one hundred and fifteen, attributed his long life to the daily use of honey. Hippocrates, the father of medicine, prescribed honey for those who wished to live long, and used it daily himself.

Perhaps the most ardent honey enthusiast of the Greek scholars was Democritus, probably the greatest physicist that ever lived. Most of the laws he established pertaining to our physical world we still rely upon today. He discovered the atom and reported that it was the basis of all matter. Like his colleagues, he became interested in the problem of extending youthful vigor beyond the middle years. He concocted a number of diets and tried them, each in turn, upon himself. His interest was not entirely academic. He once admitted that he had never been able to look upon a fine woman without a craving to possess her. Considering his country's relentless ban on love and the fact that a superior Greek simply did not allow himself to have such ideas, it is obvious that Democritus was an individualist and not susceptible to propaganda.

After many dietary regimes, he finally settled on one that included a good deal of honey. Apparently it was a sound one, for he lived to be over one hundred years of age. However, during his one hundred and ninth year he decided that he had lived quite long enough. He resolved to hasten the end by abstaining entirely from food, and informed the women of his household of his decision. Athenæus (II, 177) reported that the women raised ructions about it. They reminded Democritus that the festival of Thesmophoria, a three-day autumn feast attended only by women, was just a few days off. They implored him to postpone dying until the festival was over. Otherwise, custom would oblige them to remain at home.

Rather than deprive the women of their holiday, the venerable physicist agreed to sip a jar of hot honey and remain alive until they returned home. Since all women of that era in Greece had the legal status of a chattel and could be sold like a horse or a cow in the market place at will, and since humoring a woman was not believed to be good for her character, it is clear that the old gentleman was rather modern for his times. He obliged the ladies by postponing his demise until a more convenient time for them to mourn him.

THE ANCIENT ROMANS FEASTED UPON HONEY

The festivals of ancient Rome of Nero's day have had, through the centuries, a certain aura of immorality and wickedness, though few writers have ever taken the pains to explain the exact nature of this wickedness. We are usually given the impression that they ate too much food, drank too much wine and disported themselves in an intoxicated and unseemly manner. The prosaic item generally omitted from such accounts is the fact that many of these festivals were simply celebrations of the honey harvest and the Roman equivalent of our Thanksgiving Day in the fall of the year. Beekeeping was a major industry in ancient Rome in Nero's day, and when the honey harvest was gathered the people rejoiced and celebrated.

Naturally, when people celebrate they hold large parties and banquets. And just as many Americans in our northern cities still celebrate the apple harvest by giving parties at which a great amount of hard apple cider, mild apple cider, apple pies, apple cakes and apple candies are served, so the ancient Romans celebrated their honey harvests by consuming a great number of honey dishes and beverages. The "Roman banquet" that has enjoyed so much ill-repute always included a long list of dishes made with honey: meat and game basted with honey and served with spicy honey sauces, succulent honey cakes, rich puddings and pastries made with honey, and a variety of honey confectionery.

The "Coca-Cola" of ancient Rome was a fruit beverage made with honey, and valued for its "pick-up" qualities. Delicate honey wines were served at all feasts, and the most potent and heady beverage served at a nuptial banquet was a mixture of honey, milk and poppy juice. This beverage induced a state of euphoria—dizzy optimism and good cheer, followed by sleep and marvelous dreams. One goblet of this mixture and the Roman couple launched their marriage in the most auspicious frame of mind possible.

In warm countries where many flowers bloom in abundance almost the year around, honey harvests are gathered in the spring, summer, autumn and, sometimes, in mid-winter. So it might be said that the ancient Romans had three or four Thanksgiving Days a year. But the chief impetus for these festivals was not gastronomical but financial. Honey was an important commodity and was used as a medium for barter and exchange. The honey harvest meant prosperity. The peasant paid his taxes in honey, and bought farming implements and essential foods and materials with honey. In many Mediterranean communities honey was used almost exclusively in place of gold and silver coins. It was an almost universally acceptable medium of exchange.

Pliny the Elder, who lived in Rome between A.D. 23 and A.D. 79, has written more on the nutritional and medicinal value of honey than almost any other ancient author. He, too, believed that the daily use of honey insured long life and good health. He himself did not live to old age because he was killed during an attempt to rescue some friends caught near the path of lava overflowing in the great eruption of Vesuvius in A.D. 79—the one that obliterated Pompeii. But his views are of great interest because he was more widely traveled than many of the ancient writers and in consequence knew his world more intimately and accurately. He made frequent visits to Africa, Spain, the British Isles and the Mediterranean communities in search of material for his great *Natural History*. When he wrote about the medicinal value of honey, he had the reports and corroborations of the physicians and priests of many other countries of his time.

Like modern researchers, he apparently made use of all available state records and commercial reports to find facts. Most of his contemporaries were fond of living in seclusion and spinning yarns based upon imagination. Pliny was much impressed by the great age of the people living in the region between the Apennine mountains and the river Po, and the fact that this section was thickly populated by beekeepers. He was apparently of the conviction that there was an intimate connection between the phenomenal age of these people and their habitual use of honey.

In the seventh volume of his *Natural History*, Pliny reported that in the year A.D. 76 the tax records of this region revealed that there were one hundred and twenty-four people living in this area who had passed the century mark. Fifty-four of these men and women were one hundred years old;

fifty-seven of them were between one hundred and one hundred and ten; two of them were one hundred and twenty-five years old; and seven were one hundred and thirty-five years of age, or more. In Parma, he located five other persons over one hundred and twenty-five. In other areas of this locality he found eleven more who were over one hundred.

One might be inclined to discount this report on the ground that old people are often forgetful and do not really know their correct age, some like to boast that they are older than they actually are, and others are sincerely mistaken about it. But there are one or two significant facts that cast a different light on this matter. One of them is the all but forgotten fact that the law of the survival of the fittest held absolute sway over ancient peoples, and especially among the poor. Only the strongest children of a poor family survived and lived to maturity. The terrible plagues that swept the old world, the recurring seasons of pestilence and famine and the hardships of primitive living conditions weeded out the weakest members of a family. Those who reached maturity found marriage partners who were also the strongest members of their families. Only the strongest of their own offspring survived. And so on.

Consequently, in any ancient community there were bound to be a certain number of individuals possessing remarkable vitality and endurance—the best products of this stringent breeding process. Such individuals might well live to be one hundred and twenty-five years of age, especially if they had spent the latter part of their lives engaged in the tranquil and not too strenuous occupation of beekeeping. The fact that Pliny found his long list of centenarians living in the bee-keeping districts of ancient Rome appears to bear this out. Throughout history there has been abundant evidence that beekeepers live to a greater age than other members of their communities.

Piast, the beekeeper, who was elected King of Poland in A.D. 824 and whose family ruled Poland for several centuries with honor and distinction, lived to be one hundred and twenty years of age. The Essenes, an ancient Hebrew tribe whose occupation was beekeeping, were renowned for their honey and also for the great age of their members. Many of them passed the century mark.

The extraordinary longevity of the ancient Britons has frequently provoked comment and speculation on the part of historians. Plutarch, who lived between A.D. 46 and A.D. 120, once observed: "These Britons only begin to grow old at one hundred and twenty years of age." No doubt the laws of survival held sway over the peoples of ancient Britain as they did over the ancient Romans, producing a large number of centenarians. The moderate climate of the British Isles probably also played a part. But even more significant is the fact that the original Bardic name of Great Britain was "The Honey Isle of Beli." The British Isles, at the dawn of the Christian era, were islands of flowers and a paradise for honeybees. Beekeeping was a major industry, and honey the principal commodity of these islands. Honey was an important part of the diet of every Britisher from the King down to the poorest serf. Beeswax provided them with candles for light, and mead was their favorite beverage. When Pliny visited the British Isles he reported, "These Islanders consume great quantities of honey brew."

More recently the parish registers and tombstones in the graveyards of ancient churches in the British Isles have been studied carefully, and the following data has been unearthed about native Britishers of the sixteenth and seventeenth centuries:

Sir Owen of Scotland died at the age of one hundred and twenty-four; he left a natural son born to him when he was ninety-eight. Sir Owen lived on milk, honey, vegetables, water and wine. During the last year of his life he walked seventy-four miles in six days.

Peter Garden, a Scotsman, died at the age of one hundred and thirty-one. It was reported that he was a tall and lean person and kept the appearance of the freshness of youth until his very end.

William Ellis, of Liverpool, died on the 16th day of August, 1780, at the age of one hundred and thirty.

Mr. Eccleston, a native of Ireland, lived to the age of one hundred and forty-three, and died in the year 1691.

Colonel Thomas Winsloe, a native of Ireland, aged one hundred and forty-six, died on the 22nd day of August, 1766.

Francis Consist, a native of Yorkshire, aged one hundred and fifty, died January, 1768.

John Mount, a native of Scotland, who saw his one hundred and thirty-sixth year, died on February 27, 1776.

Thomas Parr, a native of Shropshire, who died on the 16th day of November, 1635, at the age of one hundred and fifty-two, is perhaps the most famous centenarian of the British Isles. Many stories have been written about him. It has been reported that at the age of one hundred and two he married Catherine Milton and had a child by her. At the age of one hundred and twenty, he married a widow. Longevity was a trait of Parr's family, for his grandfather, a native of Bedfordshire, died in his one hundredth year.

Parr's amorous triumphs and venerable years became well known. At the end of his life he was invited to London by the Earl of Arundel, at the request of King Charles I, who wished to meet him. Apparently the royal feast that Parr consumed was too much for him, for he died soon afterward. An autopsy was performed. The doctor who undertook the autopsy reported that Parr's viscera revealed congestion, but otherwise his internal organs were in perfect condition. Parr had always lived simply and quietly, and consumed a good deal of honey wine daily, though never to excess.

THE HONEY ISLANDS

There are many other accounts of extraordinary longevity among natives of the British Isles. It is somewhat difficult to know whether one should take such reports with a grain of salt or not. It is entirely possible, under tranquil, peaceful living conditions (plus sound nutrition practices and equally sound health habits), that among families where longevity is the rule, one or two exceptional members might live to be more than one hundred and twenty years of age. But as for a life span of one hundred and fifty-two years, one may well suspect that an extra decade or two has been added either unwittingly or with intent to deceive. It is not impossible for a man to live to such an age, though it is improbable.

But it is astonishing how often the daily use of honey appears in these stories of great age. Even modern apiarians enjoy a longer life span than other members of their communities. Furthermore, it is significant that these men reach eighty or ninety years of age in full possession of clarity of mind as well as physical vigor. Some of the more famous apiarians include François Huber, Dzierzon, Langstroth, Dr. C. C. Miller, A. I. Root, Charles Dadant, and Thomas W. Cowan, for fifty years editor of the *British Bee Journal*. As John Anderson, lecturer on beekeeping at the University of Aberdeen, summed up the matter: "Keep bees and eat honey if you want to live long. Beekeepers live longer than anybody else."

Nearly all of the life elixirs and youth elixirs that enjoyed great popularity in other centuries were made with honey. Most of the youth and love elixirs still in use in different parts of the world today are made with honey. And for centuries to come it will be used in elixirs designed to promote energy and vitality.

CHAPTER II

MODERN SECRETS OF HONEY

Honey is one of the most remarkable foods we use today. After fifty centuries or more of daily use, you might imagine that everything that could possibly be known about it had long since been unearthed. Yet honey has properties that still baffle modern scientists. The laboratory has revealed many things that were not known earlier, but the more important ones remain a mystery. Why, for instance, is honey so useful to athletes? Two thousand years ago the Greek athletes stuffed themselves with honey throughout their training period, in preparation for the Olympic games. Swiss Alpine climbers have always used great quantities of honey for weeks prior to undertaking some dangerous climb. The long-distance swimmers of the nineteen twenties and thirties did likewise before attempting to swim the English Channel or some other body of water that called for endurance.

For many years deep-sea divers have also relied on honey diets during training periods. For example, the crew that volunteered in 1937 for work on the *Lusitania* lying on the floor of the Atlantic Ocean, spent six months preparing themselves for this hazardous venture. In addition to daily exercise and a diet high in nutritive value, they gradually increased the amount of honey they consumed daily until, during the three crucial weeks before they went below, they were eating a pound and a half of comb honey for breakfast every morning!

"When we come up from the seas we are given nothing to eat except a half tumbler of strained honey, lemon juice and rain water," Captain John D. Craig of the salvage crew also revealed.

14

This report is especially interesting because the work carried out on the sunken *Lusitania* was one of the most dangerous undersea operations ever attempted and the men selected for it were the pick of the under-sea crews of the world. The dietary regime that they observed during their training period had the importance of life or death. As Captain Craig explained, "When we emerge from the water from work below, our body temperatures have fallen off from the normal 98.2 degrees to 85 degrees." Such a change in body temperature means a violent shock to the system and only by the most careful advance preparation for such work could fatal results be avoided.

The usefulness of large quantities of honey for such an undertaking might be explained on the ground that the simple sugars, levulose and dextrose, of which honey chiefly consists, helped the men to build up their reserves of glycogen and blood sugar—an important step in preparation for any feat of endurance. (Simple sugars, from whatever source, are carried by the blood stream to the liver and muscles, where they are stored as glycogen and later transformed into heat and energy.) Carbohydrates, such as honey, are also essential in the diet if the blood-sugar level of the body is to be maintained at normal. It has been well established that the blood-sugar level must always be held at a certain point, or death will promptly ensue. During periods of violent exertion, as in marathon races, tests have revealed that the blood-sugar level of an exhausted athlete tends to drop to dangerously low points. The man with the best stores of glycogen and blood sugar has the greatest endurance and emerges from the race the least fatigued.

But why honey? All starches are transformed by the digestive tract into simple sugars. If honey is useful, why wouldn't starch be just as valuable? For that matter, why wouldn't the artificial sugars and syrups also serve the same purpose? After all, the latter must also be transformed into simple sugars before they can be utilized by the body. Yet honey has been used for centuries in preference to the others for building endurance.

This question aroused the interest of W. L. Finlay, Director of Athletics of the Young Men's Christian Association of Toronto, Canada, some years ago, and extensive medical research was carried out in which members of the Walkers' Club of the Central Y.M.C.A. served as subjects. Many diets were studied and given trials for certain periods, and tests

were made of the blood-sugar levels of the athletes both
before and after competitive exercises. In the end, the medical report revealed that honey was the most useful of all
foods for raising the blood-sugar level, and concluded:

"Honey has the following advantages over other sugars:

1. It is non-irritating to the delicate membranes of the digestive tract.
2. It is assimilated rapidly and easily.
3. It spares the kidneys, lessening tissue destruction.
4. It provides a maximum of energy units with a minimum
   of shock to the digestive tract.
5. It enables the athlete to recuperate rapidly from severe
   exertion, and the men using it show less evidence of
   fatigue, according to standardized medical tests.
6. It has a natural and gentle laxative effect."

This report suggests that it is possible to use larger
amounts of honey than it would be safe to use of other
sweets, owing to the ease with which honey is assimilated.
But it does not tell the whole story. Endurance and stamina
are built up in numerous ways. Honey must make other
contributions that are important, too.

During the early days of the Battle of Britain the young
RAF pilots were given large amounts of honey in their
regular fare, and also upon returning from each mission.
Fighting at 20,000 to 35,000 feet above the earth, where the
temperature is around 15 degrees below zero and where a
man cannot live without an extra supply of oxygen for more
than a minute or so, imposes much the same physical strains
that confront the deep-sea diver, including the risk of the
"bends." Upon returning to their bases, the pilots were given
honey and water to aid them in making a prompt recovery
from fatigue. The same pilots often went aloft ten or twelve
times in one day. Here, again, we have an instance where
endurance means life or death, and where honey is heavily
relied upon to extend the normal reserves of energy.

Yet the best laboratory analyses that have been made of
honey do not reveal anything particularly unusual in its
chemical content. Dr. C. A. Browne, formerly head of the
Bureau of Chemistry and Soils of the U.S. Department of
Agriculture (now Advisor of Research), recently reported
that laboratory tests made of average American honeys
showed that such honeys contain the following:

	Per cent	Grams
Levulose (fruit sugar)	40.50	293.625
Dextrose (grape sugar)	34.02	246.645
Sucrose (cane sugar)	1.90	13.775
Water	17.70	128.325
Dextrins and gums	1.51	10.9475
Ash (iron, copper, silica, manganese, chlorine, calcium, potassium, sodium, phosphorus, sulphur, aluminum, magnesium)	0.18	1.305
	95.81	694.6225

(Based on a sample 500 cubic centimeters, total weight 725 grams, 25.6 ounces.)

(In most American honeys there is 3.73 per cent of undetermined matter.)

Levulose is the most interesting item on this list, for there are comparatively few natural sources available. Chemically pure levulose costs several dollars a pound. It is the sweetest of all sugars. It is nearly twice as sweet, for example, as cane sugar. If it could be manufactured for a modest sum it would be the ideal sugar for table use, being far sweeter than any of the sugars we have today, yet milder than any other. At the present time, honey is the richest source of levulose, and the least expensive.

All honeys vary in their levulose and dextrose content. Some have more levulose than others, as the following table will indicate. (This analysis was also made by Dr. C. A. Browne of the U.S. Department of Agriculture.)

Kind of Honey	Dextrose	Levulose
Tupelo	24.73%	48.61%
Apple	31.67	42.00
Alsike clover	36.06	40.95
Buckwheat	36.75	40.29
White clover	34.96	40.24
Alfalfa	36.85	40.24
Sweet clover	36.78	39.59

Dextrose is one of the most important energy foods we use in our daily diet. Unlike levulose, it is very common in nature, for it is found in a great variety of plants and in all parts of these plants. Dextrose can also be cheaply manufac-

tured from any starch. The fact that some percentage of
starch is found in nearly all foods is an important safeguard.
If we were not continually building up and maintaining our
storage supplies of glycogen, we would never be able to fast
for any prolonged period. Neither would we be able to call
forth tremendous reserves of energy for some emergency
when endurance might mean life or death.

THE MINERAL CONTENT OF HONEY

Until recent years few of us realized that mineral short-
ages in the diet caused a loss of energy and vitality. Modern
food researches have made it plain that the average American's diet is almost always lacking in minerals. We use
entirely too many devitalized foodstuffs that have been
robbed, through processing, of their mineral content.

The mineral value of honey is not high. It is about one
fourth that of meat and a little less than that of milk. The
dark honeys, such as buckwheat and heather, have the highest mineral content. In fact, the dark honeys have four times
as much iron as the light honeys, such as clover, orange and
sage. But as slight as the mineral value of honey may seem,
it is quite important in cases where honey is used every day
for sweetening.

An interesting experiment was undertaken some years ago
in an Austrian orphanage by Dr. A. Rolleder, who wished to
learn whether the copper, iron and manganese (which have
important blood-building functions) that honey contains in
small amounts, would have any appreciable effect upon the
hemoglobin (blood count). He selected a group of fifty-eight
boys, and gave twenty-nine of them a tablespoonful of honey
every morning and another one in the afternoon, while the
other twenty-nine boys were given none. All of them received the same diet, exercise and rest periods. The experiment was carried throughout the school year. At the end of
this period Dr. Rolleder checked the blood count of the boys
who had received the two tablespoonfuls of honey daily, and
found that the hemoglobin of nearly every boy showed an
8½ per cent increase. The control group that had not received honey showed a corresponding loss.

The famous Swiss sanatorium for children, the Frauen-
felder Home in the Canton of St. Gallen, Switzerland, undertook an even more important experiment in this direction. Dr.

P. E. Weesen of this institution chose three groups of delicate children and ordered normal foods for one group, normal foods plus honey for the second, and normal foods plus tonics and medication but no honey for the third. The group fed with honey outdistanced the other two groups in every respect: blood count, weight, energy, vivacity and general appearance.

Every time one of these experiments is undertaken—and there have been a great number in different parts of the world at different times—a fresh curiosity and speculation are revived about the "unknown" and "undetermined" matter that all honeys contain, and that still remains a mystery today. There is no question but that the benefits derived from the daily use of honey cannot be entirely explained by the known elements in honey. They always far exceed what the chemical facts would suggest. It is clear that either honey contains vital elements required by the body for health that have not yet been discovered, or else the known ingredients are combined in such proportions as to make them more valuable in nutrition than has been realized to date. All authorities in this field agree that new scientific research should be launched in an attempt to unseal the mystery. Too many researches have been made in effort to prove that honey was as good or as useful as something else, rather than to learn what it actually contains. After all, honey is manufactured in a unique manner unlike the production of any other foodstuff we use.

THE VITAMIN CONTENT OF HONEY

The pollen of many flowers has a higher vitamin C content than almost any fruit or vegetable. Honeys with the largest amount of pollen have more vitamin C than others. How much, is still a controversial matter. Years ago it was assumed that the vitamin content of honey was practically nil. Later, it was discovered that this opinion has been based on tests made with honeys that had been strained, filtered or overheated. Since many housewives assumed that honey that had a cloudy appearance must be inferior, some producers attempted filtering honeys to remove the grains of pollen that created this cloudiness, thereby removing the invaluable vitamin C content. Enlightened producers have since abandoned this practice.

In recent years new microchemical and microbiological methods, that are far more trustworthy than earlier techniques, have been developed to determine the vitamin content of foods. These new methods have shed considerable light on the vitamin content of many types of honey. One of the most important facts established was the somewhat surprising one that honey is an excellent medium for vitamins. This is not true of vegetables and fruits. Spinach, for example, will lost 50 per cent of its vitamin C content within twenty-four hours after being picked. Fruits lose their vitamin content to a marked degree during storage.

At the University Farm, St. Paul, Minn., a group of research workers, including M. H. Haydak, L. S. Palmer, M. C. Tanquary and A. E. Vivino, recently undertook new tests to ascertain the vitamins contained in a large number of American honeys. The samples were obtained from beekeepers in various localities in the United States and submitted to analysis. The University of Minnesota also had available certain samples of foreign honeys, and these samples were included in the test. The following table reveals the results:

Vitamin content of territorial United States and foreign honeys (per 100 gm.).

Origin	Nectar Source	Thiamine	Riboflavin	Ascorbic Acid	Pyridoxine	Pantothenic Acid	Nicotinic Acid
U.S.A.		µg.	µg.	mg.	µg.	µg.	mg.
Washington	clover and alfalfa	6.8	67	1.5	227	96	.24
Washington	black locust	7.4	68	1.4	233	100	.47
Washington	fireweed	8.2	81	4.1	397	56	.13
Oregon	locust	4.3	35	.5	260	103	.04
Oregon	alfalfa-sweet clover	4.3	36	1.3	430	175	.92
Oregon	fireweed	2.2	62	1.4	260	87	.84
Oregon	wild buckwheat	4.3	56	2.8	250	180	.16
California (1941)	star thistle	8.6	137	6.5	410	90	.11
California (1941)	orange	8.6	35	2.5	210	150	.16
California	sage	3.0	36	5.4	320	56	.04
California	star thistle	3.0	58	1.3	420	58	.24
Texas	cotton	2.1	58	.6	350	103	.17

Origin	Nectar Source	Thia-mine	Ribo-flavin	Ascorbic Acid	Pyri-doxine	Panto-thenic Acid	Nico-tinic Acid
Texas	rattan	6.5	87	2.3	440	190	.23
Long Island	mixed	6.5	46	2.0	240	155	.26
Florida	tupelo	4.3	58	2.1	250	118	.44
New York (1936)	buckwheat	8.6	62	1.3	250	47	.13
Tennessee	poplar	6.5	....	1.2	240	....	.14
Tennessee	crimson clover	8.6	....	2.3	400	....	.56
Idaho	dandelion	6.4	87	2.5	267	192	.11
Montana	clover	3.3	77	3.2	416	141	.18
Montana	milkwort	9.1	....	2.9	250	....	.17
Minnesota	melon	7.1	36	2.6	400	156	.58
Minnesota	mixed	6.5	....	1.9	310	....	.11
Foreign		μg.	μg.	mg.	μg.	μg.	mg.
Greece	unknown	8.6	47	2.8	460	58	.16
France	lavender	6.4	145	2.5	410	112	.82
Czech'ia	linden	9.1	62	2.5	240	56	.04
Azores	unknown	2.2	81	2.6	250	150	.33
Haiti	logwood	3.0	65	1.5	280	50	.15
Cuba	campanilla	2.2	58	1.3	420	56	.67
Guatemala	coffee plant	7.1	62	2.5	250	60	.94

This table cannot be regarded as final, for several reasons. The vitamin content of a honey varies according to whether there has been a hot, dry season or a cold, wet one in the region where the blooms were grown from which the honey-bees gather nectar. It is also affected by the chemical nature of the soil from which the flowers are grown. Moreover, there are times when the bees will consume nearly all of the pollen themselves and only a fractional amount will become blended with the honey they produce. Consequently, one batch of honey from the same farm will have a higher vitamin C content at one time than at another.

ANTI-HEMORRHAGE VALUE

One of the most unexpected developments that came about during the experiments made at the University Farm at St. Paul was the accidental discovery of the anti-hemorrhage value of honey. A test was being made in which honey was used for the prevention and cure of nutritional anemia. The subjects used for the laboratory work were chicks and rats. All young things are susceptible to hemorrhage owing to the shortage of vitamin K—the factor necessary for the production of prothrombin which controls the coagulation of the blood. Chicks are among the most susceptible. Yet in the course of the experiment the researchers noticed that after the chicks were fed with honey it became very difficult to draw from them the minute quantities of blood needed for hemoglobin tests. Their blood coagulated very rapidly.

The workers were much impressed by this detail and immediately launched a series of tests to make quite sure that it was honey which had produced this effect. A group of chicks were carefully fed so that they would be markedly deficient in vitamin K. Then these chicks were divided into small groups and fed buckwheat, alfalfa or mixed honeys. Each experiment was carried on for four days. The chicks were tested before and after being fed with honey. It was clearly established that all three types of honey had a definite anti-hemorrhage value.

THE ALKALINE SIDE OF HONEY

In recent years a good deal of stress has been laid on the importance of maintaining the proper acid-alkaline balance in the diet in order to avoid fatigue. It is well known that the principal cause of fatigue is the formation of lactic and carbonic acids in the tissues of the body following exertion. These acids must be neutralized by the alkalies of the blood. A low alkali reserve sometimes means chronic fatigue. The best prevention and cure lies in increasing the number of alkaline foodstuffs in the diet—fruits, green beans, soy beans, beets, celery and potatoes, to mention a few, in their order of importance.

The foods in which acid-forming elements predominate are beef, eggs, oysters, oatmeal, wheat, wheat flour, rice and white bread, in this order.

Recently, the Bureau of Chemistry and Soils of the U.S. Department of Agriculture tested a large number of representative American honeys to determine their potential alkalinity. It was found that the darker honeys had a higher level than the lighter ones, but that all honeys compared quite favorably with other alkaline foods. Just as oranges and lemons are acid to the taste but are nevertheless potentially alkaline, so honey is slightly acid to the palate but is an alkaline food, as the following table indicates.

Dark honey	4.5
Orange juice	4.5
Apples	3.7
Pears	3.6
Watermelon	2.7
Average dark honey	2.1
Pumpkin	1.5
Peas	1.3
Light honeys	1.0
Asparagus	0.8

(cc. normal alkali per 100 gms.)

HONEY DESTROYS BACTERIA

We know that milk is a common carrier of some diseases, and it was believed many years ago that honey might also act as a carrier. The illustrious Dr. W. G. Sackett, bacteriologist, of Colorado Agricultural College, once held this view. Confident of proving his theory, he conducted a series of elaborate experiments. He scientifically introduced into samples of honey various disease organisms that afflict human beings, to learn whether or not they would live in this medium.

To his astonishment, he found that all such micro-organisms introduced into honey died within a few hours or days —the honey destroyed them! As Dr. A. P. Sturtevant, bacteriologist of the U.S. Bureau of Entomology, Washington, D.C., later explained, honey has the peculiar and distinctive power of absorbing moisture from anything that comes in contact with it. A certain amount of moisture is necessary to maintain life in all living organisms, and when bacteria come into contact with honey, this vital amount of moisture is withdrawn and these micro-organisms die.

Dr. Sackett's experiments revealed the following discoveries:

"Typhosus was no longer present in the pure honey after 48 hours." (This is the germ that causes typhoid fever.)

"Para typhosus (A and B) were dead in the pure honey after 24 hours." (These germs cause diseases very similar to typhoid fever.)

"Enteritidis was dead in pure honey after 48 hours." (This is the germ that causes an inflammation of the intestines.)

"Dysenteriae—10 hours of exposure in pure honey was sufficient to destroy this organism." (As the name suggests, this is the germ that causes dysentery.)

"Suipestifer—the culture was dead in the pure honey on the fourth day." (The presence of this germ is often characterized by chronic broncho-pneumonia followed by septicemia.)

"Coli communis died out in pure honey on the fifth day." (The presence of this germ is said to become "pathogenic in the case of ulceration in typhoid fever. It may enter the blood, causing peritonitis.")

Many other kinds of bacteria have also been found equally vulnerable when placed in honey. The "hygroscopic" powers of honey are phenomenal. It can draw moisture from a stone crock, or even from a metal or glass container—unless these containers are treated specifically for the use of honey. During the excavations made by T. M. Davis, American explorer, of the tomb of Queen Tyi's parents in Egypt, a jar of honey was found, still in a fairly liquid state, with its characteristic aroma preserved. The jar had been hermetically sealed and placed in the tomb 3300 years ago!

It may well be, as the ancients have long believed, that honey contains some kind of "life substance" that gives it extraordinary powers.

CHAPTER III

HONEY IS SUPPLANTED BY SUGAR

Why did we, after centuries of use, abandon honey in favor of the refined sugars? It seems strange, in light of all that we know about honey today, that we discarded this nutritious sweet for the dry, sterile sugars. But many factors were responsible, including the vanity and ignorance of Europeans of the eighteenth century. Up to about 1700, very little sugar was imported to Europe from India. It cost about two dollars and a half a pound and was used almost exclusively by the royal families and upper classes. In fact, it had the social significance that caviar and champagne enjoy today. The rest of the population relied on honey for sweetening.

But just as all articles used by the nobility are greatly prized by others, so sugar became regarded as a delicacy. When means were found of manufacturing cane sugar in larger quantities, and the price was lowered, it was eagerly purchased. By 1800, England alone was importing over three hundred million pounds annually. In 1801, a German scientist by the name of Franz Achard discovered a new process for manufacturing sugar from beet roots. Soon the Continent was flooded with beet sugar. Honey began to lose prestige as a staple in the European diet.

In America, the European fashions were faithfully copied. Only members of the gentry could afford white sugar. The poor relied on molasses or brown sugar. In the farming districts, honey was a staple. New Englanders used maple sugar and maple syrup, and also a good deal of molasses.

By 1840, the industrial era was in full swing in England and in this country. New machinery was devised for refining sugar. The price was lowered. Furthermore, the industrial era brought new living habits. Debt-ridden farmers of England migrated to the factory villages and all members of their families went to work in the mills. They no longer raised their own food or tended their own bees. Huddled in factory villages, they were obliged to buy whatever food was available. Sugar was available, not honey. In America, the debt-ridden farmers were migrating to the New England and Pennsylvania factories and were also obliged to buy whatever food was available. Molasses and brown sugar were available, not honey.

By 1887, the overproduction of cane and beet sugar had become so serious that the British government sent invitations to the representatives of eight of the largest countries in Europe to discuss changing the sugar tariffs. In 1900, new inventions for manufacturing white sugar were developed in America and in England and the price was lowered to a point where most people could afford it. The annual production for the world was now over thirteen billion pounds!

Meanwhile, the immigrants that arrived in America from Europe in a steady stream between 1870 and 1914 accepted sugar as an American sweet, and something to be prized. During this period the poor of Europe had continued to rely on honey, and many of the immigrants had never used sugar until they came here.

The first World War brought sugar scarcity—and a sudden interest in honey. American farmers who kept bees were able to get higher prices for honey than ever before, and now cultivated bees in earnest. Beekeeping spread in all parts of the country. But in the meantime, mass-production methods were developed to produce war matériel, and some of these techniques were soon to be applied to the manufacture and packaging of sugar on a tremendous scale. After the war, the manufacture of sugar-sweetened crackers, candies, soft drinks and ice creams commenced at an unprecedented rate. Advertising campaigns fostered their widespread use. Nearly everyone, rich and poor alike, used white sugar for sweetening their food. Honey became a luxury—and an all but forgotten sweet.

PHYSICIANS EXPRESS THEIR CONCERN

A few physicians in this country and in Europe realized that a tragic dietary mistake was being made and from time to time wrote reports for medical journals on the ills created by the overindulgence in artificial sugars. As the consumption of refined sugars increased in the United States and in England, new digestive and nervous disorders made their appearance. In America, these were generally attributed to the new swifter pace of living. But among thoughtful medical men, it was known that the indiscriminate use of artificial sweets had a good deal more to do with these problems. Few of these men, however, cared to risk the difficulties they would create for themselves by issuing public warnings to this effect, and thus attacking the sugar interests.

Dr. Harvey W. Wiley, formerly chief chemist of the U.S. Department of Agriculture and Director of the Bureau of Foods, and one of the most courageous men that ever lived, was less hesitant. He launched a campaign to educate Americans on diet and health, and plainly stated, among other things, that the daily use of refined sugars was detrimental to health. However, the good doctor raised so much cain about other crimes against the American stomach, such as the use of injurious chemicals to preserve canned foods, the presence of meat in a state of putrefaction in sausages and potted meats, and a number of other ways in which food manufacturers once made money at the expense of public health, that his revelations about sugar were lost from view. In the course of years of struggle he was instrumental in getting the Pure Food and Drug Act written and passed by Congress. But he did not succeed in persuading Americans to use more honey instead of sugar as he hoped. The consumption of sugar in the United States grew larger year by year.

In 1929, Dr. F. G. Banting, the discoverer of insulin, delivered a forthright warning on the subject of artificial sugar, saying, "In the United States the incidence of diabetes has increased proportionately with the per capita consumption of cane sugar. In the heating and recrystallization of the natural sugar cane, something is altered which leaves the refined product a dangerous foodstuff."

Since then many eminent medical men have expressed their concern about the indiscriminate use of sugar in the modern diet and urged a return to a greater use of honey. Dr. E. P. Joslin, Professor of Medicine, Harvard Medical School, Dr. Arnold Lorand, internationally famous physician and author, Dr. J. H. Kellogg of the Battle Creek Sanatarium, Dr. B. P. Hawk, Professor of Jefferson Medical College, Philadelphia, Pa., and Dr. C. H. English, Medical Director of the Lincoln National Life Insurance Company, have all expressed their views plainly on this score. More recently Dr. Norman Jellife of Bellevue Hospital, New York City, also came forth with a candid warning about the risks involved in the injudicious use of refined sugar in the daily diet.

But for the most part these reports have been buried in medical journals, the back pages of newspapers and the minutes of private hearings. The general public has heard little or nothing about them.

A DRUG, NOT A FOOD

Few Americans know that granulated sugar, corn and maple syrups and molasses are all artificial sweets. Still less well known is the fact that they are powerful stimulants, habit forming, and actually should be classified as drugs rather than foods. We are so accustomed to using them in our daily fare that we have come to think of them as pleasant, harmless, even nourishing foodstuffs. Yet refined sugar, for example, has the same relation to food that alcohol has to milk. Alcohol can be described as a food if you want to be academic about it. It does have a calorie content that will provide heat and energy. Refined sugar has a calorie content that will also provide heat and energy. But it does not provide nourishment.

All of the artificial sugars and syrups, whether cane, corn, beet, or maple, are manufactured by a process in which all of their nutritive elements are destroyed. In the manufacture of cane sugar, for instance, the cane juice is treated with the fumes of burning sulphur, or else heated with bisulphide of lime—a process in which all of the proteins, fats, minerals, vitamins and enzymes of the natural cane juice are extracted. The sugar crystals that form are sterile. Because sugar is a devitalized product, it will keep almost indefinitely. From the shipping and storing angle, this is an important advantage. Maple syrup must also be heated to high temperatures. If its organic elements were not destroyed, the final product would soon ferment.

Honey is manufactured by honeybees from the nectars they gather from flowers. It consists primarily of two simple or natural sugars (levulose and dextrose), which are quickly absorbed into the blood stream. It also contains enzymes that aid digestion, as well as many minerals and several vitamins. Honey is an energy-building food. It contains 1600 calories to the pound, and with only one exception, surpasses all other natural foods as a source of heat and energy. The exception is the date, which has a slightly higher caloric content. Honey is six times richer in fuel value than milk. It is many times higher in fuel value than meat, fish, poultry, eggs, grains and vegetables. According to Professor Klemperer, a tablespoonful of honey is equal in caloric value to the largest sized hen's egg. And as H. W. Haggard, Professor of Physiology of Yale University, has reported, "Of all the carbohydrates, honey is one of the most rapidly assimilated." It produces energy faster than either starch or sugar, and without taxing the digestive system.

WHY SUGAR IS HABIT-FORMING

The objection to the artificial sugars, however, is not the fact that they are artificial, nor even the fact that they do not provide nourishment. After all, we eat many foods that have an entertainment rather than a nutritive value. It is the fact that the artificial sugars in their final, highly concentrated form, become powerful stimulants. They oxidize violently in the human stomach upon the slightest contact with oxygen, producing an intense explosive effect upon the digestive system, which in turn obliges the vital organs suddenly to work harder and faster.

The refined sugars might be compared to a highly combustible fuel that ignites with an explosive effect, burns at an intense heat and quickly dies out. The stimulation thus produced has a shock effect upon the nervous system as well as on the vital organs. And just as certain drugs will produce a similar stimulation—and also without providing the body with nutriment—the sense of exhilaration is shortly followed by a slump. The individual becomes aware of a hunger for more sugar—for another "lift."

This is the reason why some children, and adults also, will eat one piece of candy after another until they may have consumed an entire one-pound box of sweets. The desire for "just one more piece" becomes almost a compulsion. It is the chemical effect of refined sugar upon the digestive tract that creates this involuntary reaction. Poorly nourished children and adults are very susceptible to sugar addiction. People who suffer from nerve fatigue are the most susceptible of all types. Sugar provides a "lift." But, unfortunately, the stimulation, like that of alcohol, doesn't last and there is a craving for more. Since sugar does not provide nourishment, a dependence upon sugar for energy quickly leads to malnutrition.

While the healthy, well-nourished adult can stand the strains imposed by the daily use of artificial sugars for long periods without any apparent ill effect, just as some men can drink a pint of whiskey daily without immediately showing symptoms of illness, it is not a safe practice. Artificial sugars must be transformed by the digestive tract into simple sugars before they can be utilized by the body, and when used to excess, they place heavy demands upon the pancreas. Naturally, in many people, sugar addiction leads to exhaustion of the pancreas and diabetes makes its appearance.

Some people, however, escape this fate because they are so constituted that they can assimilate only a certain amount of artificial sugar at one time. When they consume more than they can properly utilize, the excess sugar passes unchanged through their kidneys and on into the blood stream, remaining in their systems as a poison, which causes chronic fatigue and eventually leads to kidney disease, circulatory disorders and, in some cases, a variety of digestive ills. Volumes could be written about the disorders created by the faulty assimilation of artificial sugars and syrups.

A SAFER SWEET

The daily use of honey presents no such risks or problems. It is more readily digested than either milk or fruit juices. Because it consists of natural sugars required by the body "as is," it does not have to be oxidized by the digestive tract. It is absorbed at once. Consequently, there is no excessive stimulation or shock to the nervous system or to the vital organs as there is when artificial sugar must be oxidized by the digestive apparatus. And it does not set up a craving for more. Far from being habit forming, honey, even in a very small overdose, will quickly satiate.

Despite the spectacular strides that we have made in the field of chemistry during the past forty years, we have not yet been successful in developing a sweetening as mild, safe or nutritious as honey. Our modern substitutes are not real substitutes. They are, chemically, of quite a different nature, and actually far too potent for indiscriminate use.

CHAPTER IV

HOW TO USE SWEETS INTELLIGENTLY

The value of any food depends on the man who uses it and on how he lives. It is a curious, ironic fact that the peoples of earlier civilizations would have been far better able to adjust themselves to our modern artificial sugars than are we, and we would be stronger and less nerve-ridden if we were obliged to rely entirely upon honey in order to sweeten our foods, as did they.

The peoples of other centuries were confronted with health problems that contrast sharply with our own. They were stricken down prematurely and in great numbers by cholera, smallpox, typhus, yellow fever, bubonic and other plagues. Their ignorance of hygiene and sanitation exposed them to contagious and infectious diseases. But there is reason to believe that those who escaped the plagues were far sturdier and healthier than we are and enjoyed greater endurance than we do. The rhythm of their daily lives was slow and steady, and also uneventful for long periods. Their dwellings were damp and cold, they had few diversions, and they lived chiefly on fresh-killed meat, game, fish, coarse grains and breads, honey dishes and honey brews, and in some countries on a good deal of cheese. Our artificial sugars would have fitted into their diet of coarse, heavy foodstuffs more satisfactorily than do these devitalized products into our modern fare. The danger of using a habit-forming stimulant such as granulated sugar would have been offset to a great extent by the manner in which they lived.

Modern men and women, especially Americans, are prematurely aged by functional disorders and mild infections, and die prematurely from organic diseases rather than from plagues. During the past fifty years there has been an extraordinary drop in the number of deaths in the United States caused by smallpox, scarlet fever, yellow fever, typhoid, meningitis, diphtheria and, in fact, all of the contagious or infectious diseases. This is a triumph for the microbe hunters. But during the same period there has been a dismaying increase in deaths caused by organic breakdowns such as heart disease, cancer, circulatory disorders, diabetes and diseases of the nervous system—as the U.S. Bureau of Vital Statistics can verify only too well. Each year the figures grow steadily larger. Clearly, we have gained an immense control over deadly bacteria but have made very little progress in the art of living.

Of all of the peoples of the world, we can least well afford to overindulge in the use of artificial sugars. Our tempo of living is tense and staccato, we rely on too many devitalized, predigested foods in our daily diet, and we tend to keep going on "nerves" rather than on basic vitality. This means that we are more susceptible to sugar addiction than other people. Sugar addiction always means malnutrition, because of the fact that the physiological process required for the digestion of artificial sugar interferes with the digestion of less ignitable nitrogenous materials such as proteins. The sugar addict is a "light eater" of necessity.

Yet until our chemists get busy and develop a sweet more nearly like honey in chemical content—and one that can be produced cheaply and in quantity—we shall be obliged to rely on sugar to a great extent. The world production of honey is inadequate for our needs. The answer to this dilemma is obviously a compromise. We can learn to use sweets more intelligently. And even if honey were as abundant as water, it would not be desirable, as some fanatics have proposed, to banish the artificial sugars and syrups from the face of the globe. For canning, distilling, the processing of many foodstuffs and a variety of other purposes, they are very useful. For the preparation of many dishes cooked in the home, they are more practical than honey. It is our excessive and unintelligent use of them that has made them dangerous.

We are not so physically constituted that we can safely consume such fantastic quantities of sugars. This will be clearer when you understand how many foods contain natural sugars, and that every mouthful of starch foods that we consume is transformed by the digestive tract into simple sugars.

A breakfast consisting of a glass of orange juice, a cup of coffee sweetened with granulated sugar, two slices of buttered toast and marmalade is, chemically, almost wholly sugar and water. Orange juice contains a large amount of natural sugar. The toast has a fractional amount of proteins and minerals and possibly a synthetic vitamin, but is almost wholly starch and is transformed by the digestive tract into simple sugar. The addition of marmalade, usually made with artificial sugar or syrup, provides another large dose of sugar. The only really nutritious elements in this meal are the orange juice, which has minerals and vitamins; the cream in the coffee and the butter on the toast, both of which contain minerals and vitamins, and fats that provide heat and energy. The rest of the meal is chiefly sugar.

The more starch foods you consume daily, the less sugar you need, since every particle of the starch will be transformed by your system into sugar. A luncheon consisting of sandwiches, cake and ice cream is again an overdose of sugar for your system to handle. And when you add sweetened beverages and candy to your daily fare, you are becoming a sugar addict, whether you realize this or not.

How much sugar do we need for good health? Laboratory researches point to a quarter of a pound of sugar or starch as the minimum daily requirement for an adult. The more active you are in the course of the day, the more sugar, starches and fats you need for energy. But sugar and starch become most harmful when they are used out of proportion to the amount of meat, fish, poultry, eggs, milk, cheese, grains and vegetables in your diet. These are the foods that build stamina and endurance. Sugar and starch produce heat and quick energy. When they are consumed to excess, they produce poisons and become a liability. When they are used in the place of the protective foods, malnutrition and nervous exhaustion are not far off.

Among the most desirable starch foods are brown breads, soy beans, lima beans, peas, sweet potatoes, white potatoes, oatmeal, cornmeal, and rice—to name a few. All of these starch foods have important mineral and vitamin values. They build real energy and vitality.

Your attitude toward breakfast is an excellent clue to

whether or not you are getting too much sugar as a usual thing. The person who unwittingly consumes an overdose of sugar regularly, seldom wants very much breakfast. The accumulated sugar poisons, most noticeable early in the morning, upon arising, create a heavy feeling, bad breath, a disinterest in food, or a desire only for something stimulating to drink. There are, of course, other disorders that also create these symptoms, but an overdose of sugar and starch is the commonest dietary error and the most usual cause.

When your metabolism is functioning serenely, you are hungrier at breakfast than any other time, and are capable of digesting a substantial meal. When you are suffering from sugar poisoning (also know as hyperacidity), you not only cannot eat a great deal but should not try to. Oatmeal, bacon and eggs would certainly tax your digestion. The problem is how to revise your food habits so that you can eat properly.

The answer is not simple. The cure for sugar addiction is a slow and fairly complex process. Unless you go about it properly you will not succeed, and you may make yourself quite uncomfortable.

HOW TO TAPER OFF SUGAR

You should reduce your consumption of artificial sugar— whether white or brown—very gradually. Do not try to reduce it drastically all at once. The nub of the problem is that the liver, as well as the bile and gall ducts, become adjusted to a rate of functioning established by your sugar dosage, since they are particularly susceptible to the overstimulating effects of artificial sugar. The body adjusts itself to a variety of unsuitable foods temporarily, or until an organic or functional breakdown takes place. It is not wise to remove abruptly the offending food to which the body is accustomed.

Spend some time training yourself to use just about half the amount of granulated sugar you ordinarily use to sweeten your foods. Substitute honey in every instance where this is possible. Honey will not satisfy you as a substitute for sugar if you are really addicted to the use of granulated sugar. It will not seem so sweet, and you will miss the stimulating effect of the artificial product. But try to get along with honey. At the same time, increase your intake of fruits and fruit juices.

While you are cutting down the artificial sugar in your diet, be sure to reduce temporarily the amount of highly seasoned, spiced or flavored foods that you ordinarily consume, especially chocolate, fats, and foods with rich sauces. This should be observed for about three weeks. Then you will avoid what you would call a "bilious attack."

If you are accustomed to drinking a good deal of coffee, tea or any other stimulating beverage, do *not* reduce them at the same time that you cut down your sugar quota. The same applies to smoking. Reduce it, but only slightly. Wait until you have made some progress with tapering off sugar before you launch new reforms. Violent exercises and activities that mean a great deal of nervous tension and strain should be avoided for the time being, too.

If you nibble candy between meals as a usual thing, have a box of raisins at hand and nibble them instead. Or keep a box of dates where you can reach for them at the times when you would ordinarily reach for a piece of candy. Both raisins and dates have considerable iron and phosphorus and small amounts of vitamin B_1, as well as a high sugar content (natural sugars). Thus you will get part of the sugar you crave, and you will get real nutritive values that you were not getting out of candy. Every step you take toward better nutrition, the less craving you will have for sweets.

Remember that sugar addiction means malnutrition, otherwise you would not crave stimulants or sweets. Yet the more accustomed you have become to the stimulation afforded by artificial sugars, the more difficult it is to overcome the malnutrition. For one thing, the artificial sugars interfere with the digestion of proteins, and they also change the metabolism in such a way that it is not easy to increase the protective foods very rapidly.

During the first few weeks, you will find it easier to increase the number of fruits, vegetables, and grains in your diet than proteins. If you can digest milk (some people cannot), try to increase your quota. Then eggs, fish, meat, cheese—in about this order. But all of this gradually.

The best you can hope to accomplish within the first month or so of eating less artificial sugar is a change in your metabolism which will permit a more successful use of foods that build endurance. A real foundation of energy and vitality is not acquired overnight, or by means of only a week or two of sensible fare. For the person who is habituated to artificial sugars, the process is long and slow.

At the end of the first month, you should be able to get along entirely without eating between meals, either candy, raisins, dates or sweetened beverages. You should be able to eat a breakfast that includes a whole-grain cereal, a glass of milk, an egg, or bacon, and fruits. If this does not prove to be the case, then start cutting down the starch foods in your diet, and increase the fruit and vegetables, even doubling them.

RULES FOR USING SWEETS

1. Always use the artificial sugars and syrups in a diluted form, preferably in cooked foods such as puddings, pound cake, cookies, crackers, pies, ice cream. But use these foods in moderation.
2. Use honey for sweet sauces and syrups, and for cake frostings and candy. Avoid the refined sugars in concentrated forms.
3. Never take a soft drink or a beverage sweetened with granulated sugar on an empty stomach. The sugar may be diluted, but a sweetened beverage on an empty stomach oxidizes too violently and overstimulates the system.
4. Never eat candy on an empty stomach. Use your favorite kind at the end of a meal *in place of* a dessert. Use candies made with honey.
5. Never use sweetened beverages when you are tired and want a "lift." Fruit juices will provide you with natural sugars, minerals and vitamins—and most important, the alkaline elements are what you need most to combat fatigue. Milk has the same virtues. Honey is also useful.
6. Discontinue all artificial sugars and syrups when you are coming down with a cold. Use honey, milk and fruit juices instead.

You may notice a marked similarity between these rules and those that apply to the safe use of alcoholic beverages. This is true, for the problem is quite similar.

By using artificial sugars in cooked or prepared foods rather than in concentrated forms, the overstimulating effect upon the system is lessened. Also, you are less likely to get an overdose. But remember that the more starch foods you consume, the less sugar you require. The only safe way of using sugar is to use all kinds in moderation.

CHAPTER V

HONEY FOR CHILDREN

Regardless of the food vagaries of the adult population from decade to decade, both here and abroad, honey is still considered by physicians the world over as the perfect sweet for children—the ideal milk supplement in infant feeding.

Among many modern authors, Dr. Paul Luttinger, Pediatrist of the Bronx Hospital, New York City, recorded 419 feeding cases of infants where honey was used with success and where the use of sugar would have been prejudicial. Dr. Luttinger found so many decided advantages in honey for infant feeding that he discarded other sugars. He used one to two teaspoonfuls in eight ounces of feeding mixture, substituting honey for orange juice and cod liver oil. Honey is certainly more palatable than cod liver oil; it is tasty and nourishing, and is easily and quickly digested because there is no resistance and delay in its absorption. Infants fed on honey rarely show flatulence. The facility of absorption prevents fermentation. A teaspoonful of honey to eight ounces of barley water is an excellent remedy for summer diarrhea. In marasmus, rickets, scurvy, in fact, in every case of malnutrition, honey is a *sine qua non* because it contains not only proteins but mineral salts and vitamins which are missing in sugar. The mineral content of honey is higher than that of human or cow's milk, which contain only exceedingly small quantities. Honey has a great antituberculotic reputation in infant feeding among European peasants. The sedative, hypnotic and diuretic effects of honey are well known.

Condensed milk and other proprietary milk products contain a large amount of cane sugar because it is sweeter than the appropriate milk sugar. It is a proved fact that infants brought up on condensed milk are less resistant to infections than those fed on mother's or cow's milk. Dr. R. G. Flood thinks that honey is a very valuable sugar in the treatment of constipated bottle-fed infants due to the laxative effect of the levulose faction which is slowly absorbed and eventually reaches the large intestines. Constipated infants benefited in his hands a great deal through the use of honey as a substitute.

Dr. M. W. O'Gorman, Chief of the Division of Hygiene, Department of Public Affairs of Jersey City, New Jersey, used honey for twenty-five years as a valuable addition to milk modification for infant feeding and in the growing child's dietary. The fact that many of the infants admitted to his institution had been suffering from malnutrition, some even with little chance to survive, makes his statement more impressive. His charges received at first one-half teaspoonful of honey every 24 hours and the amount was gradually increased to two teaspoonfuls, according to size and bowel movements. In case of constipation the amount of honey was increased. Honey has a decided laxative effect on infants. This effect, however, is lost if the honey is boiled.

The old Gaelic honey was reputed to have served better for children than any other tonic. The Scotch believed that honeysuckle, a favorite of the bees, contained some kind of a "life substance." The nomad Arabs, the Bedouins, feed their youths even today on buttermilk and honey. Important antituberculotic and antiscrofulotic effects were attributed to honey by the peasants of many countries. Honey and cream or butter for adolescents was considered a safeguard against tuberculosis. A glass of barley water with a tablespoonful of honey is a popular health drink for juveniles on account of its mild laxative effect. On the European continent and especially in all Slavic countries honey is still the preferred sweet for children.

SUGAR POISONING IN CHILDREN

Beyond any doubt, a great error in the present feeding methods for children is to permit them to consume sugar candy instead of natural sweets. Dr. Seale Harris (*New Orleans Med. & Surg. Journ.* 81, Sept. 1928) remarks: "The

sugar-fed child often becomes rachitic, is prone to acquire
colitis and other infections. If he survives infancy he becomes the pale, weak, undernourished child, or the fat,
flabby, indolent and self-indulgent adolescent. Sugar-saturated and vitamin-starving America presents a problem. . . .
An ounce of prevention in an infant is worth more than the
proverbial pound of cure in an adult. Sugar-fed children will
not enjoy milk, eggs, fruit and vegetables to provide them
with protein, fats, minerals and vitamins, which are needed
for their growth."

Dr. Harris thinks that the sugar-saturated American children are confirmed sugar habitués. They cover their breakfast
cereals with sugar, spread sugar-syrup over their pancakes,
heap jams over the muffins and often even sweeten their
milk. They are served sweet desserts (the sweeter the better)
for lunch and dinner. Between meals they devour candy and
ice cream, and indulge in all kinds of sweet "soft" drinks.
Candies contain 40 to 60 per cent of some sort of processed
sugars. As a result, these children suffer from flatulence,
hyperacidity and headaches and become irritable, restless,
capricious and undernourished. They are physically under-
weight or overweight and mentally precocious or retarded;
are easily fatigued and unmanageable, suffer from one cold
after another. The French Dr. Le Goff contends that about
80,000 children die in France annually from the direct effect
of industrial sugar. Dr. Le Goff would not permit in his
practice the minutest quantity of sugar in the food and drink
of infants and children. The results are astounding because
almost all the newborn grow up to robust childhood. Many
pediatrists recognize the existence of a so-called "sugar-fe-
ver."

Dr. W. E. Deeks also has found that sugar-eating children
are badly nourished, pasty-looking, irritable, restless, particularly at night, and frequently suffer from incontinence of
urine during sleep; they have decayed teeth, are constipated
at times, alternating with diarrhea; they are subject to rheumatism, chorea, recurring bronchitis and sore throat. In early
infancy they are prone to gastro-intestinal disturbances and
eczema. Sugar eaters have, as a rule, a very red and irritated
tongue; rapidly recurring hunger which is, however, quickly
and easily satisfied; a tendency to heartburn and frequent,
ineffectual belching.

The "sugar capacity" of children varies greatly. Dr. Ch. G.

Kerley, the noted pediatrist, observed in many children serious maladies which could be traced to the indiscriminate use of candy. Among the diseases he found persistent head colds, otitis, enlarged tonsils, recurrent bronchitis, bronchial asthma, vomiting, rheumatism, chorea, eczema and urticaria. Dr. Kerley found in 78 cases:

Recurrent vomiting	8
Eczema	13
Asthmatic bronchitis	7
Asthma	4
Frequent colds, coryza, tonsillitis	17
Chorea	11
Rheumatism	4
Rheumatism and endocarditis	6
Urticaria	2
Recurrent bronchitis	6

Several cases were conjoined with one or more of the other ailments. Of the group, for instance, there were combinations of:

Eczema, urticaria and rheumatism;
Eczema, urticaria and bronchial asthma;
Eczema and chorea;
Eczema and bronchitis;
Rheumatism and asthmatic bronchitis.

Most of Dr. Kerley's patients improved without medication by simply depriving them of candy. Some of the "sugar susceptibles" were so sensitive to "candy poisoning" that a small piece of candy was sufficient to produce an outbreak. "It would seem," remarks Kerley, "that to some individuals cane sugar is sufficiently toxic to produce a perversion of functions with symptoms of its own . . . and in others to produce enough change to invite or allow bacterial invasion, as in acute articular rheumatism and endocarditis."

CHAPTER VI

THE HONEYS OF MANY LANDS

The pale, amber-colored liquid sold in jars in grocery and delicatessen shops is the only honey that many people ever know. Yet there are snow-white honeys, brown honeys, honeys with purple tints, and even sea-green honeys. There are several hundred varieties produced in different parts of the world. The United States alone produces more than two hundred and fifty kinds. Of this number, only about twenty-five are distributed commercially, and most of us see but a few of these twenty-five varieties. Seventy per cent of all the honey placed on sale in the United States in peacetime years is a clover honey. When the demand for a wider range of flavors makes itself known, we will see many new honeys appear on the market.

With the coming of World War II, a curious situation developed regarding the honeys available in grocery stores. During the pre-war years, the United States produced about two hundred million pounds of honey and imported around twenty million pounds. A good part of the latter came from France, Hungary, Malta, Persia, Palestine and other famous honey-producing centers. The wartime restrictions on shipping naturally curtailed this supply. Then sugar rationing was put into effect in the United States and a new and tremendous demand for honey was felt in every part of the country. Stocks of American honeys quickly vanished. Wartime price regulations for honey induced many farmers of the big honey states of the Middle West and Far West to sell their honey in retail quantities in their own localities instead of shipping it to the large honey packers who would distribute it through retail stores in all parts of the country. Honey disappeared from grocers' shelves.

Where to obtain honey? The packers turned to Latin America and the West Indies. During the emergency, any and every kind of honey was gathered up, including honeys ordinarily sold only to bakers, and these inferior honeys were placed in jars bearing new and unfamiliar labels and rushed to the retail stores. About fifty million pounds of honey a year were obtained from these sources. Thus, nearly half of the honey available in retail stores was foreign. American honeys were all but vanishing from the market. They were being sold in the farming districts by the farmers themselves.

A few of the large packers who sold honey under well-known brand names were successful in maintaining their own standards. Through contracts with important honey producers in the western states, they were able to obtain the same superior grades for which their brands had become famous. But they were not able to get as large a quantity as desired, and they were obliged to give grocers quotas. When a grocer sold out his stock, he was required to wait his turn before he was given a new supply. Then it would sometimes happen that for a long interval only inferior foreign honeys would be available in certain neighborhoods.

Some of the honeys from Latin America are exquisite in color and flavor, and as fine as many American honeys. But very little of this high-grade honey appeared on American grocers' shelves during the wartime emergency. Most of the stock placed on sale was muddy in color, rank in taste and totally lacking bouquet. Also, many new packers entered the field, some of them grossly ignorant of the simple rules for handling this product. For example, nearly all honeys from tropical climates are very thin in consistency, and since the average housewife is certain that a thin honey is one that has been watered, many unenlightened packers tried to take care of this problem by boiling their stocks until the honey had thickened to the desired consistency! Naturally, all the flavor and bouquet went off in steam. Also, some of the honey that reached grocers' shelves during the war had actually been scorched. Thus a flavor was added that led many housewives to assume that the product had been adulterated.

Very little adulterated honey ever reaches the retail stores. The laws pertaining to this offense are stringent and are strictly enforced. For the slight additional profit that might be gained, few packers would risk the heavy fines and other penalties that would be imposed. If the label of the jar you buy carries the statement that the honey is 100 per cent pure you can be quite sure that it is. Even when this statement is omitted, you can still feel confident that the product is pure. Incidentally, the commonest ways in which honeys are ever adulterated is by the addition of sugar syrup or water, both of which all honeys contain in certain percentages anyway.

However, because honey is so often used in infant feeding, even this kind of adulteration is regarded as a serious offense. The water content and sugar content of various types of honey have been established by law and packers are obliged to abide by it.

AMERICAN HONEYS

Perhaps the finest honeys in the United States are the clover honeys of Montana, Wyoming and Minnesota. Some of these are as smooth and mellow as butterscotch and have a tantalizing, unforgettable bouquet. The honeys of the northern states are somewhat sweeter than those of the southern localities, and are also considerably thicker in consistency. To many people, the orange-blossom honey of California has the most delightful fragrance. The grapefruit blossom honey of Texas is rated by others as the finest honey of all—beautiful in color, pungent to the taste, and with a spicy bouquet.

Then there are gourmets who claim that the clover honeys of Ohio, Michigan and New York surpass all others for delicacy of flavor, an aromatic bouquet and an ideal consistency —neither thick nor thin. Some hold that the raspberry honeys of New England are more fragrant and delectable. The fireweed honeys of Washington and Oregon are highly prized by others, for they are both sweet and tart, and as thick as molasses. A few prefer the dark buckwheat honey of New York, Ohio and Michigan.

California produces the largest volume annually, and is famous for sage, alfalfa, orange-blossom and star thistle honeys. Many people assume that the South is the best honey-producing area, but this is not true. Second to California in annual honey production, are Michigan, Ohio, Wisconsin, Illinois, Iowa, New York, Texas and Minnesota. The southern regions of the United States are admirably adapted for raising bees, and many apiarists in these localities make a business of selling colonies. But the largest honey yield is obtainable in areas that have the heaviest nectar crops. Alfalfa, alsike clover, sweet clover and white clover are the most valuable nectar plants. These crops are most abundant in the northern states.

However, bees prefer to gather nectar in hot dry weather rather than cool or rainy periods. There has been a good deal of controversy as to the reason why bees will not gather nectar on rainy days. It is possible that the nectar of blossom cups becomes diluted with water or is washed away. But it has been established that the nectar flow of honey plants is sweetest and most abundant on sizzling hot days. Bees revel in such weather.

Even in areas where flowers are blooming profusely, bees travel a flight mileage of 50,000 miles to gather a single pound of honey. In regions where nectar plants are less abundant, they may fly 300,000 miles in round trips to garner a pound. As a general thing, about 37,000 nectar loads go into the production of a pound of honey.

There are more than eighteen hundred kinds of plants, trees and shrubs in the United States from which bees collect nectar. Incidentally, there are about fifty agricultural crops that are almost entirely dependent upon the service rendered by honeybees for pollination; for example, asparagus, broccoli, Brussels sprouts, cabbage, carrots, cauliflower, kale, onions, peppers, pumpkins, radishes, rutabagas, squash, turnips, and many others. Without pollination, these plants will blossom but they will not yield a crop.

The use of insecticides has greatly reduced the number of small insects in certain agricultural regions, especially in areas where insecticides are dumped by the ton over crops from airplanes. Many of these small insects played an important role in the pollination of crops. Now bees must be relied upon to a much greater extent. Some commercial fruit growers either rent or buy hundreds of swarms of bees and arrange to have the bees delivered to their orchards just as the fruit trees are coming into bloom. They know that the more completely the bees pollinate the fruit blooms, the more abundant the fruit crop will be.

Some fruit trees are self-fertile; that is, they can fertilize themselves with the aid of a light wind to mix the pollens of their blossoms. Others are self-sterile, and must be fertilized by the pollen of another strain if they are to produce fruit.

The Stayman Winesap apple tree is one of this type. Fruit trees of this kind require the services of bees for satisfactory pollination, for the wind cannot always be relied upon.

A most interesting experiment was carried out at an Experiment Station of the U.S. Department of Agriculture in 1923 to determine just how effective bees were in the pollination of fruit trees. A tent of muslin was built around one Grimes apple tree and one Stayman Winesap which were about forty feet apart in the heart of the orchard. A muslin partition was built through the center of the tent lengthwise, so that one half of each tree was on one side and one half of each tree was on the other. Bees were placed in the tent on one side of the partition, so that they could fly back and forth between the halves of the Winesap and the Grimes. No bees were placed on the other side of the partition.

On the side of the tent without bees, no fruit developed on that half of the Stayman Winesap tree. The same half of the Grimes produced a few apples, for a Grimes apple tree is self-fertile. The halves of the trees that were pollinated by bees produced an abundant fruit crop. It was clear that the services of bees are essential.

Other blossoming trees and plants that also require the services of bees if a rich harvest is desired are the almond, apple, apricot, avocado, blackberry, blueberry, cantaloupe, cherry, cranberry, gooseberry, grape, muskmelon, peach, nectarine, pear, persimmon, plum, strawberry and watermelon.

Honeys gathered from American fruit blooms vary from a white to a golden color. Some have an excellent flavor, and others are on the insipid side. But not a great deal of honey is harvested from commercial crops. Bees are brought to the fruit farms strictly for their services in the task of pollination. The honey harvest is a secondary consideration.

Some honey is used for wine and cordial manufacture; meat packers buy a good deal for curing meats; and a certain amount is used for processing tobacco.

BLENDED HONEYS

Some of the finest American honeys are sold under well-known brand names. A few of these are blended honeys. One of the most popular is a blend of the sparkling sage honey of the West, the smooth clover honeys of the Northwestern states and the superb orange-blossom honeys of California.

This blend is unforgettable. Orange-blossom honey is wonderfully fragrant, but it is too sweet to please most people "as is." By adding a rich clover honey, the blend acquires smoothness. A small amount of white sage adds a spicy tang that supports the orange-blossom flavor without destroying its bouquet.

Aside from the delightful results obtained, there is a practical reason for blending honeys. The packer who sells honey under a brand name knows that if you like his brand, you will expect every jar you buy to be exactly the same as the first one you purchased. This is quite natural, but you are asking a good deal of him.

The honey packer's problem is quite complex. Honeybees manufacture the honey he sells, and the flavor, color and texture of the product depends upon the nature of the flowers from which the bees gather nectar. It is not possible to tell a self-respecting bee that she is to confine her interests to orange-blossom nectar this spring simply because your customers are fond of orange-blossom honey. She may get a whiff of mangrove flowers carried by the breeze from a swamp near by and leave the orange orchard. Or she may discover some eucalyptus trees and develop a hankering for eucalyptus nectar (which has a medicinal flavor).

Perhaps only a small number of her more adventurous fellow workers will accompany her on this jaunt. But a tiny amount of eucalyptus nectar added to orange-blossom nectar will not improve the orange-blossom flavor. If you are providing your customers with an unblended orange-blossom honey, they will be displeased with the slight alteration in flavor. It will not do to tell them that your bees wandered off this season. They will merely suspect you of adulterating your honey.

The packer who sells a blended honey is in a more fortunate position. If the orange-blossom honey of one spring seems to have a hint of other fragrances, or is merely weak because of a cold, wet season, he can alter his formula, using more of the fine clover honeys in proportion to the orange-blossom. The almost imperceptible difference in flavor in the orange-blossom honey that might be noticed if sampled "as is" can be completely erased by the slight addition of sage honey and more clover.

Sometimes California bees are negligent about California's reputation for fine sage honey and divert themselves by gathering the nectar of wild buckwheat while harvesting a sage crop. And as buckwheat has a strong, pungent flavor and a little of it will ruin the sage honey, the person who hopes to get pure sage honey is dissatisfied. Bees of the Northwestern states will sometimes upset all man-made calculations about the honey crop by seeking out the blooms of basswood, which have a peppermint flavor. Clover honey with a peppermint flavor cannot be used for blending. The peppermint will make its flavor known regardless of the proportions used.

These are some of the problems that confront the honey packers. An energetic bee can travel at the rate of fifteen miles an hour in any direction she chooses, and she sometimes chooses to fly two miles away for a brand of nectar that catches her fancy. Ordinarily, however, bees take the line of least resistance and will gather the nectar nearest at hand. Some large producers try to control the bees' interests by destroying wild plants and shrubs within a certain area that might introduce unwanted flavors into a honey harvest.

Sometimes mixed honeys, that is to say, honeys which have been blended by the bees themselves by mixing the nectars of many wild flowers together, have subtle bouquets that are superior to one-crop honeys. But in tropical climates, where a great number of pungent swamp flowers grow in profusion, beekeepers have less luck. The honey produced from swamp flowers will be pure and wholesome, but it is too often dark in color, more acrid and biting than sweet, and frequently indistinct in fragrance. This was the chief problem with the honeys from the West Indies imported during the war years. They were nutritious and useful, but thoroughly disappointing to anyone accustomed to the superb honeys of the Middlewestern states.

FOREIGN HONEYS

France has always produced a great number of honeys of superior quality. The chemical nature of the soil of many areas of France is richer than that of the soil of most regions of the United States, and for that matter, of many other parts of the world. French vegetables have a more distinct flavor than our own, and the flowers raised in the more fertile regions are many times more aromatic than our own. The acres of marvelously fragrant jasmine flowers grown at Grasse in France have a scent that can be clearly distinguished more than a mile away. They are grown chiefly for perfume manufacture, but the thrifty French also keep bees in this region, and the honey garnered from this flower crop is world-renowned. The rosemary honeys of Narbonne and Languedoc are also greatly prized. The honey of Narbonne is crystal white, granular and highly aromatic.

The French, however, consider their sea-green honey, gathered from the blooms of gooseberry bushes and sycamore trees, a great delicacy and sell it in nearly all parts of the world. It is of unsurpassing excellence.

The acacia honey of Hungary, gathered from the nectar of acacia flowers (from which some of the sweetest perfumes are manufactured) is another famous honey that has enjoyed world-wide popularity. Malta and Persia produce a variety of unusually fine honeys. Less well known are the exotic lotus honeys of India, the snow-white honeys of Siberia and the black honeys of Brazil. From Africa comes a clear green honey that the bees produce in red combs.

One of the unique honeys of the world is the guajillo honey of Texas. The guajillo plant is an acacia shrub of the southwestern prairies and its white blooms have a delicate, piquant fragrance which is imparted to the honeys gathered from them. Guajillo honey is water-white with a subtle milky reflection. It is valued chiefly for its remarkable color.

Mexico produces some excellent honeys, especially in Yucatan. These honeys are magnificent in color, flavor and bouquet. Argentine clover honeys are similar to the top-rank clover honeys of Montana, Wyoming, Wisconsin and Minnesota.

For many centuries Scotland has supplied the world with the finest heather honey. This is extremely thick, has a purplish tint, is highly aromatic, and is valued for its unusual mineral content. Doctors frequently order it for convalescents because of its bloodbuilding properties. Eucalyptus honey from Australia, as well as from California, is frequently used for medicinal purposes.

GRANULATED HONEYS

Not all honeys are liquid. There are a few, like the Hawaiian alergoba honey, that quickly granulate. Many Europeans prefer granulated honey and regard it as a delicacy.

Most American women, however, are quite disturbed when a jar of honey develops sugar crystals and assume that it has spoiled. Actually, the crystals can be easily dissolved simply by placing the jar of honey in a bowl of warm water. In a few minutes the honey will return to its clear liquid state, its flavor and bouquet unchanged.

It is the proportions of levulose and dextrose that honey contains that determine how rapidly it will granulate. Honeys like tupelo and sage are very high in levulose and do not tend to granulate. But honeys that are high in dextrose, such as alfalfa, clover, buckwheat and many others, will form crystals fairly quickly. Packers who wish to hasten the granulation of honey so that it may be sold in solid chunks use the same techniques employed by candymakers, stirring the honey until the crystals form. Agitation, or stirring, will cause almost any honey high in dextrose to granulate rapidly.

It was Kucharenko, the famous Russian sugar chemist, who discovered a method of reversing this process, so that honeys high in dextrose would not granulate for long periods. After an elaborate series of experiments, he finally established the fact that if honey that has been removed from the comb and strained is very slowly heated to a temperature of 140° to 150° and held at this point for about half an hour, the tiny dextrose crystals which all honeys contain in varying percentages would dissolve and would not readily form again. This technique did not alter the flavor and bouquet of the honey. When honey is heated above these temperatures its nutritive values are considerably affected.

American packers welcomed this technique as the answer to an all but insoluble problem in the distribution of honey. Frequently honey granulated in transit, and when it arrived at a grocer's establishment the manager took one look at the jars and shipped the stock back to the packer. He had found from sad experience that housewives could not be convinced that the granulated honey was as good as liquid honey. Women believed that the honey had been adulterated by an addition of sugar syrup, and that it was the sugar syrup in the honey that had caused it to form sugar crystals. Actually, the addition of sugar syrup would not have this effect upon honey. It is the nature of honey itself that precipitates granulation, for its dextrose crystals are the offenders.

On the other hand, this method of processing honey to prevent granulation does not alter the honey's usefulness for making candy, frostings, and so on. When honey is heated to 238°, as it is when you are making a boiled syrup, the honey will thicken, spin a thread, and form a soft ball if dropped in cold water, just as a sugar syrup will do when used in preparing a frosting or fondant.

COMB HONEY

Many people are suspicious of all strained honeys and prefer the untouched combs for table use. With the well-known brands the suspicions are unfounded, for these companies handle honey by scientific methods, and stake a costly reputation on each jar. They will not risk jeopardizing a reputation built up over a period of decades by using an inferior honey under their brand names. But in the case of honeys sold on the highways or by unknown persons who come to your door, honey in the comb is a safer purchase than strained honey.

Every comb honey is a sealed mystery. It may prove to have an exquisite flavor and bouquet, superior to that of any strained honey, or it may be flat and insipid. After all, the flavor of honey is determined by the kind of flowers from which the bees have gathered nectar, and some blooms lack individuality in fragrance. Honey in the comb has all the fragrance the nectars possess, or the lack of it, sealed in tiny airtight compartments.

Combs that look white or a creamy white are usually the best. A brownish tinge, however, does not always indicate age. The position of a comb in the hive may affect its color. But as a general rule, the whiter a comb is, the more likely the contents will be satisfactory.

Comb honey is always higher in price than strained honey, because you must pay for the beeswax as well as the extra handling and packaging costs. Beeswax is almost as important a crop as the honey itself and brings a high price per pound.

CHAPTER VII

MOLTEN GOLD FOR YOUR TABLE

Modern meals can be made as appetizing and exciting as the feasts of the ancient Romans if you have some curiosity in this direction, and also the patience necessary to learn how to use honey in preparing a variety of dishes. Honey is not merely a sweet, but a sweet with a flavor. The flavors of different types of honeys are as subtle as the bouquets of fine wines. When honey is added to other foods, many prosaic dishes are transformed and made new and delightful.

The stickiness of honey and the difficulty of pouring it are its most objectionable features. Both offer sufficient reason for the reluctance most women have about using it for cooking. But both objections can be overcome. First, you should transfer a small portion of honey from the large container to a drip-cut pitcher, such as you use for serving maple syrup. Once you have placed honey in such a pitcher you have it under control. When you wish to use it, you can place the pitcher in a bowl or saucepan of warm (not hot) water for about ten minutes. Then you will find that it will pour in a thin drizzle instead of a heavy stream. Honey, when warmed, tends to liquefy and is much easier to handle.

Better still, when you pour honey into your drip-cut pitcher, dilute it with water. One-third of a cup of water to a cup of honey will give you a syrup of the consistency of maple syrup. All of the commercial syrups have a higher water content than honey has. One-fifth of a cup of water to a cup of honey will give a consistency like that of corn or cane syrup. Either of these dilutions will make a more satisfactory sweetener for your morning coffee, cereal, fruit drinks or waffles than undiluted honey.

But a word about flavor. A mild clover honey is best as a sweetener for coffee, tea or chocolate. It is a more neutral flavor, and of sufficient sweetness to make a good substitute for artificial sugars. The orange-blossom and sage blends are delightful in fruit drinks and as spreads for waffles, toast, biscuits, and so forth. Buckwheat honey offers a zestful and piquant change as a spread for waffles, pancakes or hot biscuits. Buckwheat honey with buckwheat cakes will take you, according to epicures, directly to Elysian fields of enchantment.

BREAKFAST USES OF HONEY

When you feel like serving something new and delicious, try this: Blend a cup of grated fresh orange peel with a cup of orange-blossom or clover honey and a pinch of salt, and let the mixture stand in a bowl over warm water for half an hour to blend the flavors. Or vary it by using a quarter of a cup of grated lemon rind, three-quarters of a cup of grated orange rind with a cup of orange-blossom or clover honey, and a pinch of salt. Either of these mixtures makes a tangy, delicious spread for toast, waffles or pancakes. Incidentally, both orange and lemon peel have a high vitamin C content and should never be wasted.

Also, try honey-butter. Blend a cup of clover honey with three-quarters of a cup of butter or margarine. Let the butter or margarine stand at room temperature until soft enough to blend with the honey. Stir until thoroughly mixed, pack in a wide-mouthed jar, cover tightly and store overnight in the refrigerator to solidify. This can be spread like butter on hot biscuits, waffles or pancakes. Always keep honey butter stored in the refrigerator when not in use, and always tightly covered; otherwise it will absorb the odors of the ice box. Try mixing a small quantity first, and vary the proportions to taste. Grated orange peel added to this mixture gives it a delicious flavor. Use half a cup of grated orange peel to each batch of honey butter.

An equally delicious spread is honey cream. For this mixture, heavy cream must be used. Heat clover honey to 130° or 140° F. and mix in cream in the proportions of about two parts honey to three parts cream. Blend carefully and pour at once into a wide-mouthed container, cover tightly and store in the refrigerator. This makes a firm but pliable spread with a delicate flavor. In many ways it is more appetizing than honey butter.

Professor P. H. Tracy of the Dairy Department of the University of Illinois invented this spread in 1932 as a new item that dairy farmers might develop as a commercial product, using 42 per cent honey and 58 per cent cream. A certain number of producers have adopted the suggestion and it is now available at many stores as "Honey-Whip." You can make it at home yourself.

Breakfast Cocoa

Blend 2 teaspoonfuls of cocoa with 2 teaspoonfuls of clover or any other mild honey, add half a cup of boiling water and cook for one minute. Add 1½ cups of hot milk to the honey and cocoa mixture, stirring constantly. You will find this makes a smoother beverage than cocoa made in other ways.

LUNCHEON DISHES

Squash Cups with New Peas

4 cups hot mashed squash	1 teaspoon salt
¼ cup honey	pinch baking powder
2 tablespoons butter	

Mix ingredients thoroughly. Place a scoop of the mixture on a dinner plate. Make a cavity on top and fill with hot peas to which have been added butter, salt and one teaspoon of honey to each cup of peas. Yield: 8 to 10 servings.

(American Honey Institute)

Sweet Potato Soufflé

1 No. 2½ tin of sweet potatoes, or	2 teaspoons honey
	3 tablespoons of butter
3 cups of freshly cooked sweet potatoes	¼ cup orange juice
	2 eggs
¼ teaspoon of salt	

Rice the cooked sweet potatoes into a mixing bowl. Add salt, honey, orange juice, egg yolks and butter, and whip thoroughly. Fold in stiffly beaten egg whites.

Heap individual mounds of this mixture on buttered baking sheet or use a pastry tube to make individual croquettes. Bake in a hot oven (425° F.) to a golden brown. Arrange croquettes on serving platter, and top each one with a preserved cherry.

(American Honey Institute)

Glazed Parsnips

Slice cooked parsnips lengthwise, making slices about ¼ inch thick. Arrange in shallow baking pan and pour over diluted honey, but not enough to cover them completely. Add one tablespoon of butter for each half dozen slices of parsnips. Place in a moderate oven (350° F.) and bake for 20 minutes, turning slices after 10 minutes. Before serving, place under the broiler for a few minutes.

(American Honey Institute)

Scalloped Tomatoes

1 can tomatoes	1 cup cracker crumbs
2 tablespoons butter	½ teaspoon salt
2 tablespoons honey	pepper to taste

Drain liquid from tomatoes and reserve for other use. Cover bottom of buttered baking dish with a layer of solid tomatoes. On this sprinkle salt, pepper, dots of butter and honey. Cover with a layer of cracker crumbs. Repeat with another layer of tomatoes, crumbs and seasoning. Bake 20 minutes in a hot oven.

(American Honey Institute)

Honey Acorn Squash

1 acorn squash	⅛ teaspoon pepper
2 teaspoons honey	⅛ teaspoon mace
¼ teaspoon salt	1 teaspoon butter

Cut squash in half lengthwise and remove seeds. Place in baking pan with ½ inch water covering bottom of pan. Spread honey over inside of squash. Add seasonings and butter. Cover. Bake in moderate oven (350° F.) about 1 hour. Uncover, brown top delicately. Serves 2.

(From the Golden Blossom Test Kitchen)

Dixie's Favorite

2 cups left-over ham, ground	1 tablespoon butter
1 can whole kernel corn	½ teaspoon mace
1 teaspoon salt	½ cup water
1 teaspoon paprika	½ cup honey
pepper	

Spread half of ground ham in bottom of buttered casserole. Mix corn with seasonings and spread over the ham. Dot with butter. Top with remaining ham. Mix honey with water and pour slowly over the top. Bake in moderate oven (300° F.) 40 minutes. Serve with cornsticks. End your meal with fruit salad and coffee.

(From the Golden Blossom Test Kitchen)

Candied Calf Tongue

1 tongue	¼ teaspoon allspice
½ cup vinegar	¼ teaspoon cinnamon
½ cup honey	¼ teaspoon cloves
½ cup seeded raisins	1 teaspoon salt

Cook tongue in boiling salted water until tender. Drain; skin. Place tongue in roasting pan. Cover with mixture of honey, vinegar, spices, salt, raisins. Simmer, covered, on top of stove, 45 minutes.

(From the Golden Blossom Test Kitchen)

Baked Ham

1 ham	1 cup honey
moist bread crumbs, about 3 cups	1½ cups crushed pineapple
	cloves

Select a nice-quality ham of desired size. Wipe with a damp cloth and remove unsightly parts. Wrap loosely in parchment paper or in similar paper which comes wrapped around the ham. Place fat side up in roasting pan. Bake at 300° F., allowing 15-20 minutes per pound if tenderized (25-30 minutes per pound if not tenderized). Then remove wrapper. Also remove skin. Rub surface completely with the crumbs. Press cloves one inch apart over the entire surface. Add honey to the pineapple and heat until hot. Pour this syrup over the ham and continue baking. Baste occasionally until a rich brown glaze is secured and ham is tender.

(American Honey Institute)

Canadian Bacon, Fruited and Honeyed

6 slices Canadian style bacon	1 cup honey
1 cup water	1 cup raisins
	6 slices pineapple

Have bacon sliced one-half inch thick. Place in dripping pan and into an oven of 350° F. Bring water to the boiling point, add the honey, stir until well mixed; then add the raisins and simmer for 10 minutes. When the meat has been in the oven 1 hour, place a slice of pineapple over each piece of bacon, pour the honey syrup containing the raisins over the bacon and pineapple. Return to the oven for 15 minutes. Especially good to serve at a buffet supper.

(American Honey Institute)

Smooth Chili con Carne (With Honey)

1 cup diced celery	1 pint water
1 cup chopped onions	1 tablespoon salt
4 cups ground beef	⅓ cup honey
1 teaspoon chili powder	1 quart cooked or canned red
1 pint tomato purée	beans

Fry beef, onions and celery slowly until done. Place beans, tomato purée, water and salt in kettle. When mixture boils, add fried meat and vegetables. Let simmer slowly for 2 hours. Add chili powder, and just before serving stir in the honey.

(American Honey Institute)

Golden Honeyed Chicken

1 frying chicken (3-3½ lbs.)	1 cup rich milk
	½ cup honey
salt, pepper	½ cup mushrooms (if desired)
flour to dredge	
4 tablespoons butter, melted	

Cut chicken into serving size pieces. Season with salt and pepper (a little cayenne may be used). Dust with flour. Arrange in flat baking dish or roaster. Pour melted butter over top. Place in hot oven, uncovered, ½ hour to brown; then reduce heat to moderate. Mix milk with honey; pour over chicken and bake 1 hour. Add mushrooms, if desired, 15 minutes before serving. Serves 4-5.

(From the Golden Blossom Test Kitchen)

Luncheon Salads

A delightful and easy way to use honey is in salads and salad dressings. Honey brings to these wholesome combinations its own inimitable flavor. Especially in fruit salads are the natural flavors of fruit and honey compatible.

Golden Salad

1 package lemon gelatin	¾ cup grated raw carrots
1 cup boiling water	½ cup crushed canned pine-
¾ cup pineapple juice	apple (well drained)
2 tablespoons lemon juice	¼ teaspoon salt
1 tablespoon honey	

Dissolve gelatin in boiling water to which salt has been added. Add pineapple juice, lemon juice and honey. Mix well and add raw carrots and pineapple. Pour in mold which has been rinsed in cold water. When thoroughly set, unmold, arrange on lettuce leaf and garnish. Yield: 8 to 10 servings.

(American Honey Institute)

Frozen Strawberry Salad

1¼ cups fresh strawberries, crushed	2 packages cream cheese
½ cup fresh pineapple, crushed or diced	2 tablespoons honey

Thoroughly blend cream cheese and honey. Add fruit and stir slightly. Put in refrigerator tray and freeze for 2 hours. Cut into squares, arrange on lettuce, or pile in parfait glasses, top with honey meringue and garnish with strawberry or sweet cherry. Yield: 6 servings.

(American Honey Institute)

Summer Salad

1 cup watermelon balls	¼ cup honey
1 cup cantaloupe or honey-dew balls	juice 1 lemon
	½ cup whipped cream

Cut balls with ball cutter (or cube the fruit of watermelon, cantaloupe or honeydew). Sprinkle with lemon juice, then honey and chill. Fold whipped cream into fruit just before serving—on crisp lettuce. Serves 4-5.

(From the Golden Blossom Test Kitchen)

French Dressing

⅓ cup salad oil	2 tablespoons honey
¼ cup lemon juice or vinegar	dash of paprika and salt

Mix in bowl or salad dressing bottle. Sprinkle 2 or 3 tablespoons of this dressing over salad bowl of greens. Toss and serve.

(From the Golden Blossom Test Kitchen)

Honey Dressing for Vegetable Salads

1 cup salad oil	1 teaspoon salt
½ cup catsup	1 teaspoon paprika
⅓ cup vinegar	1 teaspoon grated onion
⅓ cup honey	1 clove garlic, cut in half

Measure ingredients into salad dressing bottle. Shake well. Let stand 10 minutes. Remove the garlic. Use as needed—keeps indefinitely.

(From the Golden Blossom Test Kitchen)

Boiled Honey Dressing

1 egg	1 tablespoon cornstarch
4 tablespoons melted butter	½ teaspoon mustard
½ cup vinegar	2 tablespoons honey
1 tablespoon flour	1 cup milk
1 teaspoon salt	dash cayenne pepper

Melt butter in top of double boiler. Add flour and cornstarch and stir to a smooth paste. Add milk slowly, stirring constantly to prevent lumping. Let cook until thick. Add salt, pepper, honey, mustard and vinegar to beaten egg and stir into the thickened mixture. Cook until thick, stirring constantly. This may be diluted with whipped cream and honey.

(American Honey Institute)

DESSERTS

Milk and Honey Golden Custard

2 eggs, slightly beaten	1 pt. scalded milk
⅓ cup honey	1 teaspoon vanilla
⅛ teaspoon salt	1 tablespoon butter

Add honey to the eggs. Stir in the hot milk gradually and beat well. Add salt and vanilla. Pour into 6 buttered custard cups. Dot top with butter. Bake in moderate oven (350° F.) about 35 minutes—until set through center. Serve in custard cups or cool and turn out on serving dishes and surround with fresh fruit.

Children call this "Candy Custard." Place a teaspoon of honey in the bottom of each custard cup before filling with custard mixture. When baked, turn out on serving dish, the carmelized honey forming a beautiful brown sauce over top.

(From the Golden Blossom Test Kitchen)

Honey Baked Pears

8 pear halves	1 teaspoon cinnamon
¼ cup lemon juice	2 tablespoons butter
½ cup honey	

Arrange pears in shallow buttered baking dish. Pour the lemon juice and honey over them. Sprinkle with cinnamon and dot with butter. Bake in moderate oven at 350° F. Serve hot with cream as dessert. Peaches prepared this way also make a delicious dessert.

(American Honey Institute)

Honey Baked Apples

Wash and core the apples. Leave part of the core in the bottom of the apples to act as a plug. Fill the cavity with honey, using as much as the tartness of the apples requires. For variety, add a bit of lemon juice, or a few cinnamon candies. You may stuff the cavity with raisins and dates or other fruit combinations.

Baked Fragrant Grapefruit

2 grapefruits	½ cup honey

Cut grapefruit in half. Remove seeds and center. Trickle honey over top of each. Bake in moderately slow oven (300° F.) about 15 minutes.

Chilled Honeyed Grapefruit

Core grapefruit and chill. Just before serving, fill center with honey.

LUNCHEON BREADS

Honey Pecan Rolls

½ cup butter	1 cup pecan halves
1 cup honey	white bread dough

When dough is light, punch down and let stand a few minutes. Roll out in sheet one-half inch thick. Brush with butter and spread with honey. Roll and seal edge firmly. Cut into one-inch slices. In bottom of the baking tin, place butter cut into small pieces. Spread honey over butter and scatter on the pecans. Place rolls one inch apart on the honey and butter mixture. Cover and let rise until double in bulk. Bake in moderate oven (375° F.) 20 to 25 minutes. Let rolls stand in pans 1 minute after baking before turning them out.

(American Honey Institute)

Honey Currant Muffins

4 tablespoons shortening	2 cups flour
3 tablespoons honey	3 teaspoons baking powder
1 egg	½ teaspoon salt
½ cup currants	¾ cup milk

Cream shortening; stir in honey, mix well. Add egg and beat well. Stir in the currants. Sift together flour, baking powder and salt. Add to first mixture alternately with the milk. Fill greased muffin tins two-thirds full. Bake in quick oven (400° F.) about 20 minutes. Makes 12 large muffins.

(From the Golden Blossom Test Kitchen)

Quick Marmalade

Plunge dried apricots into hot water, or if they are so dry that they are hard, soak in hot water for 5 minutes. Drain and run through food grinder (fine knife). To each cup of ground apricots add 1½ cups honey (liquid or solid). Blend thoroughly. Store in sterilized jars at least two weeks. This forms a spread of marmalade texture. Delicious on toast, hot biscuits, or as a filling for French Toast sandwiches.

(American Honey Institute)

Marmalade Biscuits

These biscuits have the appearance of up-side-down biscuits, are easy to make and very good. Cut biscuits as usual (baking-powder type), make indentation in each biscuit, and put a teaspoon of Quick Marmalade in each cavity. Brush with butter and bake in the usual manner.

Golden Honey and Apricot Mousse

1 large can apricots   1½ cups cream, whipped
1½ cups honey   juice of 1 lemon
2 egg whites, stiffly beaten

Drain apricots and rub through sieve. Add honey and lemon
juice. Fold in stiffly beaten egg whites and then the whipped
cream. Pour into refrigerator tray and freeze without stirring.
Serves 10 to 12.

(From the Golden Blossom Test Kitchen)

Tea Pastries

2 cups flour   ½ cup cold shortening
1 teaspoon salt   (half butter)
¼ teaspoon baking powder   1 cup moist cottage cheese
                             2 tablespoons honey

Sift dry ingredients together, cut in shortening. Add honey to
cottage cheese and mix well. Add to flour and mix lightly to
smooth dough. Roll thin on lightly floured pastry board. Makes 3
dozens pastries.

Honey Pecan Pastries

1 cup honey   1 cup raisins, chopped fine
1 cup pecans, chopped fine   juice 1 lemon
4 tablespoons crumbs

Mix. Place spoonful of filling on two-inch squares of pastry.
Form into triangles—or draw four corners to top. Press edges together. Bake in oven (350° F.), 25 minutes.

Honey Cherry Tea Tarts

1 can red pie cherries,   honey
  drained of all juice

Cut pastry with cookie cutter and line very small tart pans. Fill
with 4 or 5 red cherries. Cover each with honey. Bake in slow
oven (300° F.) about 25 minutes.

(From the Golden Blossom Test Kitchen)

EUROPEAN DISHES MADE WITH HONEY

Backlava (Turkish)

1 lb. almonds (ground)	pie pastry
¼ lb. butter	honey syrup
3 cups of fine sugar	

Mix ground almonds, butter and sugar into paste.

Use regular pie pastry made with hard-wheat flour (use less shortening than ordinarily) and roll out ten paper-thin layers, spread each one with almond paste, stack one on top of another. The top and bottom layer should be thicker than the others. Press outer edges firmly together. Cut diagonal gashes over the surface. Move stack to cookie sheet and bake in a fairly hot oven.

To serve, cut in small diagonals, and spoon over each one a tablespoon or so of honey syrup. (Serves 10.)

Honey syrup: Use equal parts sugar and honey, add a small pat of butter, with a stick of cinnamon, and cook until mixture spins a thread. Cool before using.

(Courtesy Miss Sally Larkin, *American Cookery*)

Biscomes (French)

½ lb. honey	5 ounces almonds (blanched
¼ cup of sugar	and chopped)
flour	½ teaspoon powdered cinnamon

Mix honey, sugar, chopped almonds and cinnamon together. Work in enough flour to make a paste so firm that it will leave the sides of the dish clean.

Knead well until soft and pliable. Roll out to paper thickness on lightly floured board, cut with biscuit cutter and bake on greased cookie sheets in an oven at about 400° F. Cool on cake rack until crisp. Serve warm. These are delicious crackly-crisp honey biscuits. Recipe makes about 40-50 medium-sized cookies.

(Courtesy Miss Sally Larkin, *American Cookery*)

Zabaglione (Italian)

yolks of 3 eggs	½ cup plus 1 teaspoon Marsala
3 tablespoonfuls of honey	or Madeira wine

Put the yolks of eggs in a bowl and beat until they are light in color, gradually add honey, continue to beat. Then add the wine and mix thoroughly. Pour into saucepan and cook over high heat, beating incessantly without allowing mixture to boil or thicken. As soon as it begins to rise, remove from heat and pour into glasses. When served cold, keep in cold place until required. Serves 4.

(Courtesy Miss Sally Larkin, *American Cookery*)

Rödgröd Med Flöde (*Danish*)

1 lb. red currants	*2 ounces sago flour*
½ lb. red raspberries	*few black currants*
water	

Stew cleaned fruits with just a little water, enough to prevent burning. Strain off juice, mix a little with sago flour and add rest of juice. Cook until thickened, stirring constantly. Then remove from heat, stirring continuously until almost cold. Pour into serving dishes. Top with whipped cream sweetened with honey.

(Courtesy Miss Sally Larkin, *American Cookery*)

CAKE BAKING WITH HONEY

Some cakes are greatly improved by being made with honey. Nearly all breads and rolls have superior keeping qualities if made with honey; which is one reason why a good many thousands of gallons of honey are sold to commercial bakers every year. However, at the risk of appearing inconsistent and unreasonable, we admit that we do not think the average layer cake is much improved by being made with honey instead of granulated sugar. There are expert cooks who can turn out a perfect layer cake made with honey instead of sugar, but for the average housewife honey is a liability, not an asset, in cake-making. The final product is too moist, even soggy, or it is not sweet enough.

Artificial sugar is least objectionable in a diluted form, as when used in making cake. This is an instance where it does the stomach very little harm, and does the cake a great deal of good. When it comes to the frosting of the cake—that is another matter. Delicious frostings can be made with honey instead of granulated sugar, and it is in such concentrated forms—as icings, syrups, sauces, etc.—that the artificial sugars are most potent and dangerous. Try the following frostings made with honey.

Honey Meringue Frosting

2 egg whites	*½ cup honey*

Measure honey into mixing bowl. Add egg whites and beat with (electric) rotary beater about 10 minutes until frosting stands in peaks. Add pastel vegetable colorings and any desired flavoring. This frosting will keep in refrigerator for days. (Note: when hand rotary is used instead of electric whip, measure honey into small saucepan and heat gently for 10 minutes. Cool slightly, then add egg whites and beat with hand rotary until frosting stands in peaks.) Grated orange rind makes a delicious flavoring.

(From the Golden Blossom Test Kitchen)

Boiled Honey Frosting

1½ cups honey   1 egg white
⅛ teaspoon salt   ½ teaspoon vanilla

Cook honey and salt to 238° F., or until it will spin a thread or make a soft ball when dropped into cold water. Beat egg white. Pour the syrup in a thin stream over the beaten egg white, continuing to beat until all syrup is added and frosting stands in peaks. Add vanilla and spread on cake.

(American Honey Institute)

"Ten-Minute" Honey Frosting

1 cup honey   ⅛ teaspoon salt
¾ cup sugar   1 teaspoon flavoring, if desired
2 egg whites   coloring, if desired

Measure honey into top of double boiler. Simmer over low heat, 10 minutes. Add sugar and egg whites. Beat with rotary egg beater, over rapidly boiling water, 10 minutes, until frosting piles high. Add flavoring if desired—½ teaspoon of peppermint essence, or grated orange rind. But the delicate bouquet of honey is itself an enjoyable flavor.

(From the Golden Blossom Test Kitchen)

Honey Orange Filling

1 tablespoon flour   ½ cup honey
2 tablespoons cornstarch   ¼ teaspoon salt
2 egg yolks, well beaten

Mix smooth in double boiler. Add slowly the following, stirring constantly: ¼ cup orange juice, 2 tablespoons water, 1 tablespoon lemon juice.

Add 1 teaspoon butter and grated rind of ½ orange. Cook over boiling water, stirring occasionally until thick (about 20 minutes). Cool and spread between layers of cake.

CHAPTER VIII

THE NECTAR OF THE GODS

The ancients spent a great deal more time quaffing beverages, both alcoholic and non-alcoholic, than we are prone to do today. There was more time for all things—including the custom of sipping on all possible occasions the cup that cheers. Moreover, in many regions of the Old World, fresh, sweet clear water was very difficult to obtain. A great variety of beverages were made when water was plentiful and carefully stored for dry periods. Most of the ancient wines were made with honey. Grapes did not come into common use in wine making until much later.

But honey is most nutritious when used "as is" in beverages. The delightful fragrance and flavor of the clover, sage and fruit-blossom honeys make an important difference in the taste of fruit drinks. They acquire nuances, or perhaps what a musician would call overtones, of a delectable variety. An ordinary orangeade can be transformed by the addition of orange-blossom honey to sweeten it. Go a step further and add a pony of cointreau and garnish with a sprig of mint, and you will have something to quaff on a hot day that will make summer weather seem most agreeable. A New Year's Day eggnog made in the old Knickerbocker Dutch fashion with honey (and brandy) can make you wish that New Year's Day arrived more often.

The very consistency of honey makes it blend more smoothly with beverages than does ordinary granulated sugar. Here are some suggestions for hot-weather drinks:

Lemon Tingle

1 quart picnic lemonade   2 teaspoons honey mint syrup
1 quart ginger ale

Yield: 6 servings (iced-tea-glass size). For an individual serving use equal portions of honey, lemonade and ginger ale and add ⅓ teaspoon honey mint syrup.

¼ cup honey   1 teaspoon mint extract or mint
2 tablespoons lemon juice   leaves to flavor

Combine honey and lemon juice, add mint, store in refrigerator. Use in lemon tingle or in other fruit punches.

Fruit Punch

1 cup honey   1½ cups freshly made, strong
1 cup orange juice   tea
½ cup lemon juice   ⅛ teaspoon salt
1 cup crushed fresh fruit   1 pint ginger ale

Mix all the ingredients except the ginger ale. Just before serving, add chopped ice and the ginger ale. If the punch is too strong, add ice water in small quantities until the punch is the flavor desired.

Refreshing Party Drink

1 quart currants   1 small stick cinnamon
1 pint water   5 oranges
1 cup honey   3 lemons

Wash currants, place in a kettle and cover with water. Reserve ¼ cup currants for garnishing. Simmer gently for 10 minutes. Strain. If a clear juice is desired, do not press the pulp. Combine the pint of water, honey and cinnamon and boil 5 minutes. Remove the spice stick. Combine the juice of the oranges and lemons and the currant juice with the spiced syrup, diluted to taste. Fresh pineapple or cranberry juice may be used. Serve hot or cold.

Honey Iced Chocolate

2 tablespoons cocoa   3 tablespoons honey
½ teaspoon salt   2 cups scalded milk

Blend cocoa, salt and honey. Add to scalded milk and simmer for 5 minutes. Pour over chipped ice. Top with honey meringue or whipped cream. Yield: 3 servings.

Honey Lemonade

1 cup honey	½ cup strained lemon juice
1 quart water	⅛ teaspoon salt

Mix the honey with hot or cold water, depending upon whether a hot or a cold drink is desired; add the lemon juice and salt. Serve with cracked ice if cold drink is desired.

Pep Cocktail

1 egg	juice 1 orange
1 tablespoon honey	juice ½ lemon

Beat egg yolk, honey and fruit juice with rotary beater until fluffy. Fold in egg white, stiffly beaten. Serve in sherbet glass. This is a real "pick up" with staying powers.

In wintertime a hot spicy drink lifts the spirits, and takes the chill off a raw, bitter day. The very aroma is invigorating. Try the following:

Hot Honey Punch

¾ cup honey	1 can (No. 2) pineapple juice
1½ cups water	juice 2 lemons
¼ teaspoon salt	12 maraschino cherries with
½ dozen cloves	syrup
1-2 inches stick cinnamon	1 seedless orange, thinly sliced
2 cups strong hot tea	

Combine honey, water and spices. Simmer 5 minutes; strain. Add juices and tea. Bring to boil; add cherries and sliced orange. Makes 10 cups.

Dr. Beck's Hot Punch

1 quart old sherry	1 quart water
whole cloves	allspice
cinnamon sticks	salt
honey	

Mix sherry and water, add spices to taste, and about two cups of honey (or less according to taste). Boil very slowly for 2 hours. Allow mixture to stand 24 hours. Strain and serve hot.

THE MEAD OF THE ANCIENTS

Honey and water, called hydromel, is one of the oldest drinks known. It was later called mead, meth, or metheglin.

There are three distinct kinds of mead, the simple, the compound and the vinous. *Simple mead* is made of water and honey which does not undergo fermentation. It is made by boiling about three parts of water to one part of honey; the honey may be increased or diminished according to taste. The boiling is done over a slow fire until one third has evaporated, then the remainder is skimmed and put into a cask, until the cask is full. In three or four days it will be fit for use. Simple mead is a favorite drink of the Mohammedans who are forbidden alcoholic beverages.

Compound mead is made in the following manner: While the simple mead is boiling, some raisins, cut in two, are cooked separately, allowing one-half pound of raisins to six pounds of honey. During the time while the boiling mead is diminishing, the liquefied raisins are added through a coarse linen filter and the mixture is boiled together for a short time; a toasted crust of bread, steeped in beer, is then put into it and after the scum, which forms afresh, has been removed the liquid is soon taken off the fire and allowed to settle. After it has been poured into a barrel (new barrels must be rinsed with brandy), an ounce of salt of tartar, dissolved in a glass of brandy, is added. Kept in a warm room or exposed to the sun, with the barrel open, it will commence to ferment. Some pieces of lemon peel, a few drops of essence of cinnamon and some syrup of gooseberries, cherries, strawberries and aromatic flowers may be mixed with the concoction to suit individual taste. The froth must always be replaced with some of the remaining stock and the barrel kept continually filled. Compound mead ferments a considerable time, usually about two months. After the fermentation has ceased, the bung-hole is closed. The longer the mead is aged the better and more potent will it be. After several years in a cask it may be put, with the addition of a lump of sugar, into bottles which then must be well corked.

For the preparation of *Vinous mead* there are more diversified instructions, rules and procedures than for all other alcoholic liquors combined. Every nation, every class and age has had a different method of mead-making. The component parts, the technic and innumerable other considerations, had to be carefully bethought to produce an excellent mead. One Greek mead contained thirty-six ingredients and was called "true nectar." The ancients depended even on the constellations of stars to select the best time for preparing this favorite drink. The fermentation period of mead was of such vital importance with some races that during that time sexual abstinence had to be observed, otherwise it was believed the mead would spoil. The number of ingredients which were selected is simply amazing. Thyme, ginger, nutmeg, cinnamon, cloves, pepper, sesame flour, sweet marjoram, rosemary, even whites of eggs, were added. In later centuries whisky, brandy and gin were used to strengthen and flavor it. Even the water was of consequence. Pliny, for instance, advised (Libr. XIV. ch. 20) in making hydromel the use of rain water which had to be at least five years old.* The *thalassiomel* of the Greeks was prepared with sea-water.

The pervading principle in the innumerable orthodox procedures of mead making was to determine first the correct proportion of honey, water and other ingredients; the period of time and the slowness of boiling; the vessel (copper, glass or earthenware); the proper scumming of the froth; the time and manner of fermentation and stirring; and finally how long to let it stand until it had aged enough and was fit to drink (Saxon quality).

Dr. Bevan's recipe for making mead was a typical *modus operandi:* "Dissolve an ounce of cream of tartar in five gallons of boiling water, pour the solution off clear upon twenty pounds of fine honey, boil them together, and remove the scum as it rises. Towards the end of the boiling add an ounce of fine hops; about ten minutes afterwards put the liquor into a tub to cool. When reduced to a temperature of 70° or 80° Fahrenheit, according to the season, add a slice of toasted bread smeared over with a little yeast, the less the better because *yeast invariably spoils the flavor of wines.* If there is a sufficiency of extractive matter among the ingredients employed, yeast should not be introduced; nor if it is fermented in wooden vessels. The liquors should now stand in a warm room, and be stirred occasionally. As soon as it begins to carry a bead it should be tunned and the cask filled up from time to time from the reserve, till the fermentation has subsided. It should now be bunged down, leaving open a small

---

* Tickner Edwardes, even today, makes his mead with rain water.

peghole; in a few days this may also be closed and in about
twelve months the wine will be fit to bottle."

The invert sugars, dextrose and levulose, which honeys
contain, readily produce alcohol by fermentation. Saccharose
(sucrose), the main component of cane-sugar, must first be
inverted before it ferments.

The celestial nectar, the drink of the gods, was really
fermented hydromel, that is, honey-wine, which was only
later called mead or meth. Mead is often mentioned in the
Bible and in the sacred books of India. Abraham à Santa
Clara called the bees (Judas IV. 14) the "little mead-brewers." The wide-spread popularity of mead is best proven by
the philologists. In Scythia it was called medos; in Greece,
methu; in India, madhu; in England, mead; in Old Irish,
mid; in German, meth; in the Slavic countries, medu; in
Lithuanian, medus; etc.

Previous to the introduction of grape wine and malt liquors, mead was a universal drink the world over. It was
prized in the remote past as good wine, beer, whisky and
cordials are today. Mead preceded in Greece the wine-era by
many long centuries. Aristotle remarks: "When the honey is
squeezed out of the combs an agreeable strong drink, like
wine, is produced." Beer drinking among the ancient Greeks
was considered a barbaric custom. Apollonius Rhodius (235
B.C.) related that the Argonauts kept vast stores of food and
mead which the cup-bearers drew forth in beakers and described how the heroes grasped the full goblet in both hands
and relished it, pouring also a cup of mead upon the seas
before lifting their anchors. The Nordic races highly valued
mead and it was the drink of their heroes. The Niebelungen
heroes drank meth out of golden goblets and ox-horns. The
high halls of Valhalla flowed with mead and the dead warriors freely drank from the inexhaustible supply. The intrepid
Goth, Beowulf, was offered mead by the bracelet-covered
queen at the court of Hrothgar who made the hall the
greatest mead-house ever known. Mead was the "nectar" of
all Scandinavian countries. It was their national drink. On an
ancient Runic calendar, found in Scandinavia, consisting of
pictorial symbols, two of the twelve months of the year bear
witness to the popularity of mead. January first, the day of
Yuletide festivities, was represented by two crossed ornamen-
tal meadhorns (these embellished horns look very much like
those from which visitors in Upsala [Sweden] drink mead

today [for a good price] at the "Barrow of Odin"), and the month of September, by a beehive and a swarm of bees, a reminder to collect the honey which is so necessary for brewing mead. In the Eddas, mead is often mentioned. Speaking of heroes: "Blue mead was their liquor, and it proved their poison; they marched to Cattraeth filled with mead and drunk." In the early Christian era mead still was a favorite drink. In the *"Legends of the Holy Rood,"* mead is also mentioned. Chaucer alludes to "meth" as a common drink (*Knight's Tale; Miller's Tale*). Shakespeare alludes to metheglin when he suggests something sweet (*Love's Labour's Lost; The Merry Wives of Windsor*).

It seems rather remarkable how mead, the first fermented drink known, was ousted by the fermented produce of grapes, namely, wine. It suffered the same fate as honey as a food and sweetening substance. Wine prepared from grapes came into vogue comparatively late. Grapes came from China to Greece and Sicily; the Phoenicians carried them to the South of France, and the Romans to the Rhine and Danube. The first grape vines were planted on the Rhine in Ludwigsau by King Ludwig, "The German," in 842 A.D. But it required many centuries before mead was entirely "dethroned."

Among primitive races, especially the African tribes, mead has remained, up to this day, the popular drink. The East-African nomadic races not only eat the wild honey but they dilute it with water and let it ferment into wine or beer called *tetsch,* which is their favorite drink. The African soothsayers and prophets intoxicate themselves with this honeywine. During ceremonials and magical practices it is liberally used. They drink it from horns, like the Niebelungen used to do, and also distil it for brandy.

In Africa honey is found in huge quantities; in some places the bees are so numerous, as Seyffert-Dresden describes it, that they even obstruct the passage of travelers and the air is filled with the odor of honey and the continuous buzzing of bees. The African races, without exception, are fond of honey. They mix it with flour, cereals, butter, milk and bake pastries with it; they even knead their tobacco with honey, making dry cubes for chewing-tobacco which they call *Latuka.*

The Boros and the American Indians of the Western Amazon forests are also fond of honey. They use it for food and prepare their beverages from it, which they drink in excess during festive occasions. The wild honey is collected from the cavities of dead trees or from the hollow tree-trunks which the natives set up in the *thatch* of their houses for the new swarms to nest in.

In India, honey is an important article in the preparation of foods and drinks, especially in the manufacture of alcoholic liquors. The Himalayan mead has an unusual potency; one cup is sufficiently intoxicating. In ancient Babylon, date and honey-wine, called *sikaru*, was a powerful alcoholic drink. The *misshu* of the Koreans is a brandy with a high percentage of alcohol. It is a distilled honey-wine. Some Persians have a tube gently inserted between their teeth while still asleep, and have a mixture of warm milk, whisky and honey poured into their mouths so that the taste of "nectar" should be their first conscious sensation each day (*Patrick Balfour, Grand Tour*).

According to ancient Anglo-Saxon history, the beehive supplied the whole population, from the king down to the poorest subject, with food, drink and light. Mead was served at the royal tables, in monasteries and in the houses of the poor. During royal festivities, mead was served in horns. English history mentions how Ethelstan, the subordinate King of Kent (Xth Century), expressed his delight, when visiting his relative, that there was "no deficiency of mead." The affluent supply of mead in medieval Germany is proven by the fact that when hostile tribes tried to burn the town of Meissen, on the Upper-Elbe, in the year 1015, its population, owing to shortage of water, extinguished the flames with their reserve stock of mead.

J. Magnus, in the *Historia Sueonum* (The History of Swedes), describes how Hunding, the 23rd King of Sweadland, upon a false report of the death of his brother-in-law, Hading, King of Denmark, invited all his nobility to a sumptuous feast and provided a large vessel of mead. After they had become drunk, as a token of friendship for his supposedly dead friend, Hunding plunged into the vessel and *willingly* drowned himself. The Swedes considered him immortal and superior in courage to the Greek and Roman heroes.

Many varieties of honey-brew were used during the Middle Ages. Frequently the crushed combs were steeped in water, strained, and then put into earthen vessels until the liquid fermented and became mead. It was preferably kept in wooden barrels, and the longer it aged the more it gained in flavor and strength. This was the most common procedure. The stronger and "more generous" kind of mead was called metheglin. In its preparation spices, like thyme, sweet marjoram, rosemary, ginger, cinnamon, bay leaves, cloves and pepper were used in liberal proportions. Sometimes sweet apples, pears and quinces were added. In some parts of Wales, the refuse-combs were brewed with malt or spices. The drink was called *braggots,* derived from the old English brag, meaning malt, and gots, honeycomb. This was later corrupted to *brackets.* The Irish had a honey-wine called *usquebaugh.* In Ireland mead was often mixed with the "milk" of the hazel nut. Muffet alluded to this beverage, made of honey, wine and herbs, as "not unfit for a nation that feeds on flesh raw, or but half sod."

Charles Butler gave long and detailed directions about how to make the best mead—*Queen Elizabeth's Metheglin.* Queen Elizabeth was extremely fond of mead. She had her own formulas for its preparation and mellowing, and it was specially prepared for her. Let Butler tell all about this Royal drink:

"He who liketh to know the many and sundry makings of this wholesome drink must learn it of the ancient Britains: who therein do pass all other people.* One excellent receipt I will here recite: and it is of that which our renowned Queen Elizabeth, of happy memory, did so well like, that she would every year have a vessel of it.

"The Queen's Metheglin. First, gather a bushel of sweet-briar leaves, and a bushel of thyme, half a bushel of rosemary, and a peck of bay-leaves. Seethe all these (being well washed) in a furnace (not less than 120 gallons) of fair water; let them boil the space of half an hour, or better: and then pour out all the water and herbs into a vat, and let it stand until it be but milk warm: then strain the water from the herbs, and take to every six gallons of water one gallon of the finest honey, and put it into the boorne, and labor it together half an hour: then let it stand two days, stirring it well twice or thrice each day. Then take the liquor and boil it anew: and when it doth seeth, skim it as long as there remaineth any dross. When it is clear, put it into the vat as before, and

---

* The Poles have frequently been distinguished as the best mead-makers in the world.

there let it be cooled. You must then have in readiness a
kiv(e) of new ale or beer, which as soon as you have emptied,
suddenly whelm it upside down, and set it up again, and
presently put in the metheglin, and let it stand three days
a-working. And then turn it up in barrels, tying at every
taphole (by a pack thread) a little bag of beaten cloves and
mace, to the value of an ounce. Such was the mead of good
Queen Bess." N.B. "It must stand half a year before it is
drunk."

Honey-brew mixed with mulberry juice was called, among
the Britons, *morat*. This was the drink of the better classes.
Another beverage, called *pigment*, brewed from the purest
honey, flavored with spices, like ginger, cinnamon, nutmeg,
clove, etc., mixed sometimes with wine, was the drink of the
Anglo-Saxon monarchs during their customary four daily
feasts. William I reduced the number of daily court orgies to
a single state banquet. The English monks were allowed for
dinner one sextarium of mead (in modern measure this would
amount to several gallons) among six of them, and half the
quantity for supper. The Polish monks of St. Basil were
experts in making *miodomel*, a species of mead flavored with
hops. It was considered an excellent digestive and a remedy
for gout and rheumatism. *Krupnik* was another Polish drink,
made from good whisky boiled with honey, which had to be
drunk hot during the cold winter. The order of Cluny called
mead *bochet* and designated it as "potus dulcissimus" (sweetest beverage), agreeable to the taste and smell. It was ever
so much favored by these monks during great church festivities. The Russians brewed mead with a decoction of hops and
barley. The Russian *lipez* was brewed from delicious linden-
honey.

Edwards describes, in *The Lore of the Honey-Bee*, how,
during the Norman invasion, the "outlandish liquor of grape"
was brought in and took the place of the good old English
honey-brew, the Saxon mead. From that time on, he relates,
mead has steadily declined in vogue until it has become an
almost lost art, practiced only by some old-fashioned folks in
remote country places. Those who have had the good fortune
to taste the old mead, well matured in wood, are sure to feel
regret that no determined effort is made to rehabilitate it in
national favor. There is no more wholesome drink in the
world, and certainly none requiring less technical skill in the
making. All ancient books on beekeeping give directions for

its manufacture, differing only in the variety of ingredients which were added for its improvement, or rather, for its degradation. The finest mead can be brewed from pure honey and water alone. Any addition of spices or other material serves to destroy its unique flavor.

During the sixteenth and seventeenth centuries, certain beemasters were renowned in their day for mead brewing. One of the best mead-brewers claimed that his potion was absolutely indistinguishable, even by the most competent judges, from old *Canary Sack* (sack, a kind of wine, was a popular drink in Shakespeare's days). This authority gave careful directions for the manufacture of mead. If kept for a number of years, such mead, when poured into a glass, frothed like champagne, stilling soon, leaving the glass lined with sparkling air bubbles. It was of a pale golden color and had a bouquet like old cider, but its delicate taste was hardly comparable with any other known liquor. Dryden suggested diluting stronger wines with mead:

> T' allay the strength and hardness of the wine,
> Let with old Bacchus, new Metheglin join.

In the courts of the Princes of Wales, the Mead-Maker was the eleventh dignitary, preceding even the court physician. He received his land and horses free; the Queen supplied him with linen and the King, with woolen clothing. A certain amount of mead was his allotted share. In the principality of Wales, "the spacious halls of the Princes resounded, accompanied by the lyre, with the praises of mead." Mead-hall and mead-bench are often mentioned in songs of the Druid bards. There were three things in Court which had to be communicated to the king before they were made known to any other person:

> "1st, Every sentence of the judge;
> 2nd, Every new song; and
> 3rd, Every cask of mead."

Innumerable drinks were prepared from honey and wine. The famous old *athole brose* consisted of equal parts of honey and cream, to which mature Scotch whisky was added. (This was supposed to cure all ills—even without faith.) Boswell, in *The Life of Johnson,* mentioned a drink, "a curious liquor peculiar to his country," which the Cornish fishermen drank. They called it *mahogany*. It consisted of two parts of gin and one part of treacle, well beaten together. Johnson begged Mr. Eliot to have some made, which was done with proper skill. Johnson thought it a very good beverage, a counterpart of what was called *athol porridge* in the Highlands of Scotland, a mixture of whisky and honey, but he considered the latter a better liquor than that of the folks of Cornish, because "both of its component parts were better." (It is not surprising that Johnson suffered from bad gout.) Johnson remarked that "mahogany must be a modern name, for it is not long since the wood called mahogany was known in this country." Johnson also had the bees in mind when he remarked that "Tom Birch is as brisk as a bee in conversation."

Edwardes quotes the old bee-master: "But of all the good things given us by the wise physician of the hive, there is nothing so good as well-brewed metheglin. This is just as I have made it for forty years, and as my father made it long before that. Between us we have been brewing mead for more than a century. It is almost a lost art now; but here in Sussex there are still a few antiquated folks who make it, and some even remember the old 'methers,' the ancient cups, it used to be quaffed from. As an everyday drink for workingmen, wholesome, nourishing and cheering, there is nothing like it in or out of the Empire." Joseph Warder, a physician (1726), dedicating a book about bees to his ruler, Queen Anne, refers to mead as a "liquor no ways inferior to the best of Wines coming either from France or Spain," and suggests a toast to her Majesty's health "not with the expensive wine of our enemies but with a glass such as our Bees can procure us." Rev. Thorley also thought mead "not inferior to the 'Best' of foreign Wines." Honey-beer was very popular with the ancient Gauls. They had two kinds, *zythus* prepared with pure honey for the rich, and *corma*, made from the combs after the honey had been extracted, for consumption by the poor. The Russian *miod* is an old-fashioned honey-drink, of the same strength as beer.

The French being ardent wine growers, despised mead. It was never sold under that name. Nonetheless, much mead was sold in France under fictitious names like Rota, Madeira, Malmsey, etc. The Bavarian meth was the precursor of the beer industry of München. The use of hops in beer-making originated in Russia.

THE MEDICINAL VALUE OF MEAD AND OF OTHER HONEY-DRINKS

HYDROMEL, i.e., honey and water, made under the special direction of Pliny and Galen, was for centuries not only a popular drink but a salutary medicine. Pliny was a firm believer in hydromel; he thought that "it is an extremely wholesome beverage for invalids who take nothing but light diet; it invigorates the body, is soothing to the mouth and stomach, but by its refreshing properties allays feverish heats. It is well suited for persons of chilly temperament or of a weak and pusillanimous constitution, . . . diminishing also the asperities of the mind." According to Pliny, anger, sadness and all other afflictions of the mind can be modified by diet. *OXYMEL*, made of honey, vinegar, sea salt and rain-water, was in great vogue in olden times, when it was considered an infallible cure for sciatica, gout, and rheumatic ailments. It was also used to "gargarize with in *Squinancy*." There were many other preparations made with honey. *RHODOMEL* was a mixture of roses and honey; *OMPHACOMEL* was made from fermented grape-juice and honey; and *OENO-MEL* from unfermented grape-juice and honey. This last combination was used for gout and "nerves." Clysma of honey and water was considered a remedy of merit for cleansing the bowels. The ancient Greek *conditum* was honey mixed with wine and pepper. It was a popular medicine for all kinds of digestive ailments. Most ancients attributed to honey-drinks a soporiferous effect.

Butler thought that the virtues of mead were about the same as those of honey. He advocated old mead as "a wine most agreeable to the stomach, as it restores appetite, opens the passages for the Spirit and breath, and softens the bellies." He also thought that it was good for those who have coughs or quartan ague and that it helped to guard against diseases of the brain.

For many centuries mead was considered a veritable "elixir vitae." Its principal medicinal value was in kidney ailments, as an excellent diuretic without disastrous effects upon the kidneys. As for gout and rheumatism, mead ranked not only as a curative but also as a preventive medicine. It was widely used as a good digestive and laxative.

Vinegar is another profitable by-product of honey and it far excels in quality all similar products, not excepting wine vinegar. Inferior types of honey can be well utilized for this purpose. Any liquid containing sugar can be used for making vinegar. Five parts of water to one part of honey exposed to acidous fermentation will produce vinegar. It should be boiled for about 10 minutes in a jug or glass container (never metal). Some minerals and a little yeast can be added to hasten the process. Left in a barrel, in a warm room, the bunghole closed with cheesecloth, the fermentation will be complete after several weeks.

Honey vinegar, pure or mixed with honey (oxymel), also had wide employment in ancient therapeutics, both as a medicine and as an external application.

CHAPTER IX

BEEKEEPING FOR PROFIT AND FUN

Beekeeping is one of the most fascinating and absorbing occupations open to men and women today. Bees have a
unique life of their own, every colony is governed by politics
as distinctive as the man-made variety, and successful hive
management depends upon your ability to get acquainted
with the laws of the hive. This means patient study on your
part. You will find it one of the most diverting hobbies you
have ever undertaken.

Whether or not you are in a position to keep bees depends
largely upon your frame of mind rather than your place of
residence, your acreage or lack of acreage. Bees can be kept
in the back yard of a suburban home or on the roof of an
apartment building in the city. For more than two centuries
beekeeping has been profitably carried on in the heart of
New York City—the last place you might think of for raising
bees. Quite a few city dwellers still keep hives on convenient
rooftops. Central Park, back-yard gardens and the many
small parks throughout the city provide the bees with nectar
plants, trees and shrubs. Enthusiastic beekeepers are to be
found in small towns and cities in nearly all parts of the
United States. Farming communities offer, of course, the best
beekeeping opportunities.

Beekeeping can be very happily combined with other occupations. Outside of an occasional "look-see" during spring
and fall, bees require little or no attention. In wintertime the
hives should not be disturbed for any reason. It is during the
peak of the summer months that bees need care and a
watchful eye. Even then, the work involved in hive manage-

ment could be successfully handled by youngsters of school age. It is light, simple work requiring sharp powers of observation and a scholarly bent rather than hard labor. And it is so interesting that few beekeepers regard the chores to be performed as "work."

Beekeeping is not dangerous unless you unwittingly make it so. Your bees will live and let live. But there are a few exceedingly important rules to be obeyed to the letter if you wish to avoid bee stings. Bees have an unusually sharp sense of smell and dislike certain odors, such as the odor of perspiration, tobacco and alcohol. A beekeeper with halitosis will drive his bees to a frenzy, especially if he should make the mistake of breathing on them while bending over a hive. An onion breath is likewise unforgiveable. The bees will attack the offender mercilessly. Perfumes are also taboo. Even the mild scent of rouge and lipstick are disturbing to bees and will provoke their anger. There are other simple rules to be learned and faithfully observed; but as a general thing, bees will not molest a beekeeper who is considerate of them.

Bees can be kept as far north as Alaska and as far south as the equator. The best honey-producing areas of this country, however, are New York, Pennsylvania, Ohio, Indiana, Michigan, Wisconsin, Minnesota and the mountain areas of the West. The territory within one hundred miles of Los Angeles, California, is excellent. It is from this locality that honey is sent by the carload to the East.

The amount of honey that a colony will produce each year is naturally affected by the profusion of blooms near the hive. But if you should take a casual look around your town or suburb and fail to note many flowers, remember that your bees are better informed. If you live in one of the above-mentioned states there are probably a great number of small wild flowers in open lots, back yards and city parks, as well as in open fields. In addition to fruit trees, there are many other trees and shrubs that have blooms in the spring and early summer—in all likelihood, unnoticed by you. Bees will travel, in any case, a distance of two miles if necessary, to gather nectar. The less traveling they have to do, the more honey they can produce. But the average back-lot beekeeper of a small city or town harvests between fifty and one hundred pounds of surplus honey a season.

If you will take the trouble to learn the most up to date methods of beekeeping, you may increase this yield (provided, of course, that there are sufficient nectar plants in your locality) to two hundreds pounds of honey a season per hive. Under special conditions and ideal management, the yield may be stepped up to three hundred or even five hundred pounds per hive.

YOUR DEBUT AS A BEEKEEPER

When you have achieved the proper frame of mind for launching your career as a beekeeper, the A. I. Root Company, Medina, Ohio, can supply you with a copy of *Starting Right With Bees,* price 50 cents. This is a clear, comprehensive handbook on how to start your first colony of bees. It warns you to begin with just one hive, a minimum of equipment, and of the simplest kind. The book is a thoughtful, considered piece of work that will answer the very questions you will want to ask an expert.

Another excellent book which you will find helpful is *Beekeeping for Profit and Pleasure,* by Addison Webb, New York lawyer, who raised bees on his penthouse terrace near Central Park. Mr. Webb outlines in simple terms each of the steps the beginner should take as a beekeeper. This book costs $2.00 and may be obtained in any bookstore. Before you buy your bees and equipment you should read one or both of these books carefully, thoughtfully, making notes as you go along. As both suggest, you should also visit an experienced beekeeper for a day or several days and get acquainted with the appliances and methods used in beekeeping. You will gather a fund of information from the beekeeper that will be invaluable. But there is no substitute for study. It is not a mere coincidence that throughout the centuries beekeepers have always been somewhat more alert and intelligent than the average member of their communities. Both qualities are required for beekeeping.

THE OCCUPANTS OF YOUR HIVE

To the untrained observer all bees look pretty much alike. But each hive has three types.

The queen, which is larger than any of the others and is

distinguished by her wasplike figure and her long, slightly tapering abdomen. She is the center of all activities in the hive, but is not its "boss" or governor. The queen's sole duty is to lay eggs. During the peak of the season she lays between one thousand and two thousand eggs a day. She has a sting, but never uses it except to attack a rival queen.

Of the three types, the worker bees are the smallest and most numerous. They establish the law and act as a police force in the hive. They are incomplete females and cannot lay fertile eggs. They provide the wax for the comb, build the comb, gather nectar and deposit it in the cells of the comb, and evaporate it by fanning it with their wings. They also tend the young, feed the queen and the drones, and guard the hive from attack by robber bees.

The drones are male bees and are very much larger than the worker bees, but not as long and narrow as the queen. The drone has a massive look, is somewhat fuzzy and is quite harmless. He has no sting. Neither is his tongue designed for gathering nectar. Consequently, he performs no labors on behalf of the hive. He can, however, buzz more loudly and noisily than other members of the hive. Drones are produced in seemingly large numbers, considering that probably only one in many thousands finds a queen and mates with her. The worker bees tolerate the drones until the season is well advanced and then shove them out of the hive. Once the workers are assured that the hive has a fertile queen, their patience with the drones comes abruptly to an end. Since the drone cannot feed himself, he soon dies of starvation.

The worker bees themselves die within five or six weeks after birth, for they literally work themselves to death. The queen has the longest life of any member of the hive. Ordinarily, she has a life span of four or five years. Beekeepers usually dispense with her services after the second year, however, and replace her with a younger queen.

It will take you time to get thoroughly acquainted with the life in the hive, the conduct of the bees, and the role you should play as beekeeper. In fact, from the day you get your first hive, you will discover that you have in reality launched a study program that will take many years to complete. This is not because bees are difficult to raise, for they are not, but because there are so many fascinating things to learn about them and their problems.

WHEN TO START

It is just as well to wait until spring is well advanced and there are fruit trees in bloom in your vicinity before you buy your bees. If you live south of the Ohio area, do not start your first hive until the middle of April. If you live north of the Ohio area, wait until at least the first of May. In any case, pray for a warm spring. The bees do not care for cold weather.

Bees are purchased by the pound and come in packages containing three thousand bees to a pound. You will need about nine thousand bees to start your hive and you should therefore purchase a three-pound package. If you can obtain bees from a nearby beekeeper, hive and all, try to do so—but not from one too close by. His establishment should be more than two miles from your place; otherwise his bees will return home. Be sure to inquire whether his hives have been recently inspected by the state apiary inspectors and whether he can show you a certificate of health. Bee breeders are subject to state regulations and inspection, and their hives are periodically examined by an official bee inspector and certified. If their bees become diseased, a certificate is withheld, and they are not permitted to sell bees.

In the event that you are not acquainted with a beekeeper in your locality, write to the Department of Agriculture of your state for a list of bee breeders in your vicinity. Or write for a sample copy of *Gleanings in Bee Culture,* Medina, Ohio, and study the advertisements of bee breeders. Choose the one nearest the place where you live. The less traveling the bees must do, the better. Also, the less of an adjustment they are obliged to make in the way of a change of climate, the better. Bees obtained from an established breeder are more likely to be gentle and in good condition than bees obtained at random from a farmer who merely sells you bees as an accommodation.

Many authorities favor Italian bees, for they affirm that race and heredity are all in their favor. Italian bees are the easiest of all kinds for the beginner to handle. They are gentle, industrious, inclined to be prolific breeders, and have a high resistance to disease. They are distinguished by two or three yellow bands on the forward segments of the abdomen. Some strains have five yellow bands.

LOCATING YOUR HIVE

Bees are almost human in their reactions to the weather. Left to their own devices, they will build a home in a hollow log or tree trunk deep in the woods and will choose the spot with care. They do not like too much sun, too much wind, or any exposed place where they will suffer from the severe cold in midwinter. When you look about for a lively spot for your hive, choose one that offers some shade, but not too much. An orchard or vineyard offers the ideal situation. Have the entrance of the hive face a southerly direction. But when you do so, consider all the factors.

"Making a bee line" is more than a figure of speech. Bees do fly in a direct line to and from the entrance of their hive. Therefore the entrance should not face a pathway or road where people may be walking or riding by. If this is unavoidable, then be sure there is a high fence between the hive and the roadway so that the bees will be obliged to fly high above pedestrians in order to reach their hive. Don't locate the hive near a neighbor's wash line, for bees have an affinity for wet garments. And, of course, do not locate a hive in a field with horses or cattle. The animals may be stung and the hives will be knocked over.

If you do not have a high fence, a hedge, a shed or building near which to locate your hive where it can be sheltered from the cold winds of winter, it may be advisable to place the hive in an attic. In this case, place the hive close to an outside wall of the attic, with a small entrance for the hive cut through the siding so that the bees may go in or out at any time. There should also be a window near by to give plenty of light. In almost every large city there are bees kept in attics or on roofs. The attic, however, is one of the best solutions for the beginner.

You may be tempted to build your hive yourself, but we must urge you not to try to do so until you have had some experience with beekeeping. Bees will adapt themselves to both plain and fancy architecture, and will store honey in their new home, regardless of its design, as their instinct impels them to do. But, unless the hive is properly constructed, you will not be able to remove their surplus honey without destroying them. Furthermore, if the design of the interior fails to provide satisfactory ventilation, your bees will move out.

succession of dramas, all of them interesting and thought-provoking. Before the season is over you will understand why beekeepers with fifty years of experience behind them still find this occupation absorbing and could not be persuaded to abandon it.

EQUIPMENT NEEDED

There are four essential items you should buy before you obtain your bees. The first of these is a bee smoker, which consists of a small fire box, or tiny stove, mounted on a pair of bellows. A puff of smoke at the entrance of the hive and a few puffs under the cover will quiet your bees whenever you wish to examine the hive. A bee smoker costs between 85 cents and $1.25.

Just as necessary is a bee veil made of a fine mesh netting or of wire screen attached to cloth which may be adjusted to your hat, to protect your face and neck. In any case, the comfort of a well-constructed veil will give you poise, and you will not make that slapping gesture which infuriates the bees (who may be flying peacefully by with no intent or interest in harming you). Cloth veils cost between 80 cents and $1.10, and wire-mesh veils cost between $1.10 and $1.25.

Bee gloves are also indispensable. They differ from ordinary gloves in that they have very long gauntlets that come well over the coatsleeve and fasten snugly. They are made of stingproof fabrics. The usual cost is $1.00 for the fabric style, $2.00 for the leather style. The latter is soft and flexible.

An optional piece of equipment is a bee suit made of a stiff material like duck cloth. It comes in white, and is designed so that there are no tiny openings through which an adventurous bee might crawl. The openings are closed by zippers, sleeves are closed off by means of draw strings. These coveralls cost $3.85; sizes 42–44.

The fourth essential item is a hive tool. You could use a screw driver or a wide-bladed putty knife, but a hive tool is especially designed for working with hives and is worth the 65 cents that it costs, in the ease and efficiency with which you can open and adjust the inner sections of the hive.

You can, of course, study bee catalogues and find a long list of items that you feel you must have, but the ones just described are the essential ones. After you have worked with bees for a while, you will learn what additional items will be most useful to you. Talk it over, if possible, with a near-by beekeeper and learn from him how many of these items he has found helpful. He may be able to give you many practical suggestions.

BEE STINGS

There are bound to be times when you are careless or absentminded around your hive and you will get stung. What do you do then? Is there any special secret remedy for bee stings?

Despite the fifteen thousand years of beekeeping and the many thousands of prescriptions passed on from generation to generation in all parts of the world, the answer to this question is: "No, there is none." When you are stung by a bee you should immediately brush off or scrape off the sting the bee has left with you. The sting has a tiny sac of poison at its base. By brushing the sting off rather than picking it out, you may avoid breaking the sac, and thus no poison will be forced into the wound and you will be much more comfortable. The only other known method of obtaining relief is by hot compresses.

Incidentally, you have lost a bee. Once a bee stings an animal or a human being, it soon dies, for in the process of stinging it loses not only the barb, but its sheath and encasing muscles. Remember that the best way of avoiding depleting your hive in this manner is to avoid giving your bees reason for stinging you.

There are a few simple rules to observe when you must go near your hive.

1. Wear your beekeeping outfit.
2. Learn to walk and move quietly, slowly and gently when near the hive.
3. Make your visit to the hives between 10 A.M. and 2 P.M., when the greatest number of the worker bees are out in the fields.
4. Choose a bright sunny day. Bees are often in an ill humor on cool, wet or overcast days; they do not fly in large numbers foraging for nectar but frequently sulk near the hive.
5. Never make a slapping motion at a bee flying near you. This gesture infuriates bees. The offended bee you have

threatened may let out a yell of anger that will bring hundreds of others to the scene to her defense.

6. Make sure your clothes and person are free of odors of any kind.

7. Avoid breathing on your bees when you bend over the hive, since the slightest odor may disturb them.

8. Take care not to pinch or injure a bee while manipulating the hive. The entire colony may think it necessary to rescue her and drive you away.

9. Use your smoker when you anticipate trouble. This will lull and quiet the bees.

10. If you feel calm, your presence is less likely to disturb the bees. Always act as if you do, and set a good example.

CHAPTER X

THE WANDERING BEEKEEPERS

One is apt to think of a beekeeper as a fixture in his community. But there are nomadic beekeepers too. In the fall of the year many beekeepers of the northern states gather up their hives, stack them in a commodious truck and drive south. During the winter months, when northern bees are keeping each other warm in hives that are closed for business until spring arrives, the bees of the nomadic keeper are busy among the orange-blossom groves of Flordia. As the season advances, the nomadic beekeepers begin to drive north, stopping at the large commercial fruit orchards on the way. By the time they reach home, the early summer blooms of the North are well started. In this manner, the nomadic beekeepers gather three or four harvests of honey annually.

This is not a practice established in modern times, but a custom of great antiquity. The beekeepers of ancient Egypt placed the hives on boats and drifted along the Nile to provide the bees with fresh flowers which grew on the banks of the receding river, especially on its expansive delta. There was hardly any other pasturage for the bees in Egypt; there were no forests or meadows with wild flowers. Ancient Egypt had less vegetation than present-day Egypt, because a considerable number of plants have been imported during the past thousands of years. On the other hand, the lotus, brought in all likelihood from India, and considered sacred, was more extensively cultivated than it is today, when it is nearing extinction. Lotus honey was in great favor in ancient Egypt.

The inhabitants of Lower Egypt well knew that the blooming of fruit trees and flowers of Upper Egypt preceded theirs by several months. Toward the end of October, the villagers embarked on boats or rafts, packed with pyramided hives, and conveyed them down the Nile into Upper Egypt, just at the time when the inundations had subsided and the flowers had begun to bud. The bees soon exhausted the supply of nectar two or five miles around a new locality; then the floats were moved to another station and remained there as long as it proved desirable. These wanderers returned to their homes about February, the hives well-stocked with honey, gathered from the orange blossoms of Said and Arabian jessamine. The hives were carefully numbered and delivered to their respective owners. Niebuhr reported seeing such a flotilla of four thousand hives on the Nile.

We learn from the Zenon papyri that the Egyptians had wandering beekeepers even on land. These papyri, originating from the third century B.C., were discovered in 1914 by peasants digging for antiquities on the site of ancient Philadelphia on the edge of the Fayoum. Zenon was a high official of Apolloneos who sent him to Philadelphia when Egypt was under Greek influence. In one of the papyri there is an appeal of the beekeepers to Zenon, entreating him to return the donkeys which they had lent him and which they needed at once to bring home their hives from distant fields. Some farmers threatened the beekeepers that they would ruin the hives because it was necessary to burn the brushwood and inundate the fields. "The donkeys were loaned for only ten days"—said the petition—"and now it is eighteen days and the donkeys have not been returned." They begged Zenon to deliver the donkeys with the assurance that after the hives had been brought home they would be immediately returned in case he needed them. "We pay a large tax to the King and if the donkeys are not restored at once the tax will be lost. May you prosper."

The Greeks imitated the custom of the Egyptians. Columella describes how the inhabitants of Achaia took their hives overseas as far as the Attic peninsula to avail themselves of the benefits of its wonderful pastures. Solon mentioned bee caravans and bee floats in 600 B.C., and his laws demanded that each group of hives should be kept three hundred feet apart. It would not be surprising if the Egyptians journeyed as far as Greece with their hives. The ancient Greeks called the Egyptian bees "cecropic" bees. Cecrops was an Egyptian, who, about 1500 B.C., wandered to Greece and probably introduced apiculture.

The Romans, in the third century, took their hives with them to old Alemannia, and drifted down the Rhine. Wandering beekeepers have been known since earliest times. Pliny reported that when the local sources of honey were exhausted, the inhabitants of Hostilia, a village on the Po, placed their hives on boats and sailed during the night five miles upstream, where next day the bees helped themselves in their new location. The temporary stations were changed each night, until the bees had collected so much honey that the boats were heavily laden. Then the villagers drifted downstream, homeward-bound. The French "bee barges," with a capacity of sixty to a hundred hives, were frequently referred to. The Provence and the forests of Orleans were covered during certain seasons with visiting hives.

The same antiquated custom prevailed in the Mississippi Valley, starting from New Orleans. The blossoms of the river willows yielded excellent virgin honey. Perrine, of Chicago, traveled in a large boat up the Mississippi from New Orleans to St. Paul, anticipating that the shores, after the flood had receded, would supply ample pasturage for the bees. The scorching heat, however, ruined his plans; he was even compelled to pour water over the hives, which alone destroyed many colonies.

That this procedure was known also in England is shown by an article published in the London *Times*, 1830: "As the small sailing vessel was proceeding up the Channel from the coast of Cornwall and running near land, some of the sailors noticed a swarm of bees on the island; they steered for it, landed, and after they succeeded in hiving the bees they took them on board and proceeded on their voyage. As they sailed along the shore, the bees constantly flew from the vessel to the land to collect honey and returned again to their floating hive; and this was continued all the way up the Channel."

On land, the hives were placed on wagons and when the combs were filled, the traveling beekeepers returned home. In Palestine, the orange groves of Jaffa offered a rich pasturage. The hives were carried by night on camels, sixteen hives to a load. Such journeying was called "giving the bees a pasture." In medieval Spain, they had similar customs except that the hives were transported on mules. The Russians and Armenians around the Black Sea traveled like nomads, migrating with thousands of hives, pitching their tents where abundant wild flowers were to be found. Such bee-caravans, ambulatory establishments like gipsy-hordes, are often described in Greece, Italy, Germany, Austria and France. In Scotland, they conveyed the hives on carts to the Highlands, when the supply of nectar in the Lowlands was exhausted. The luxuriant blooms of the mountain heather, which last over two months, supplied plentiful nectar to the bees in the autumn when no other flowers are available. The shepherds and gamekeepers took the hives under their protection for a modest sum; as a rule, a shilling a hive. Wandering beekeepers were also known in Switzerland, where the hives were taken to the valleys when the buckwheat, which produces excellent dark honey, was blooming. In the Luneburger Heide, nomadic troupes of beekeepers were traditional, especially in springtime and late summer. The ancient laws gave them every protection.

CHAPTER XI

THE MEDICINAL VALUE OF HONEY

1. IN ANCIENT THERAPEUTICS

To subdivide the dietetic and medicinal values of honey is rather a difficult task. Wholesome food preserves health and likewise prevents or aids the cure of a disease. The advantages attributed to honey as an aliment apply as well to its medicinal properties. The rapid assimilation of invert sugars which honey contains makes it, for instance, a desirable source of quick energy, a practical food and, at the same time, an effective heart stimulant.

The use of honey as an internal and external remedial agent must be much older than the history of medicine itself; it is, beyond doubt, the oldest panacea. While primeval man had to search first and probe the curative effects of the various organic and inorganic substances, honey, the greatest delicacy of Nature within his easy reach, surely could not have escaped his attention very long and he must soon have become convinced of its supreme curative value.

In the most ancient scripts we already find references to honey as a glorified food, an ingredient of favored drinks, a popular medicine and the principal component of liniments and plasters. The oldest mythologies praised the invigorating and health-giving qualities of honey. Many allusions were made to its magic healing power.

The Bible (both the Old and New Testaments), the Talmud, the Koran, the sacred books of India, China, Persia and Egypt, all speak of honey in laudatory terms, as a food, beverage and medicine.

Honey is frequently mentioned in the Bible. Solomon in his Proverbs (24:13) advises: "My son, eat thou honey, for it is good." The Jews advocated honey as a producer of wit and intellect; it was supposed to make one "mentally keen." Moses, when exposed in the fields, sucked honey from a pebble (Exod. R. 23:8). The resuscitating and invigorating effects of honey are disclosed in the Bible. Jonathan, the son of Saul, had his eyes enlightened with the aid of honey, after which he had a better understanding of the people than his father had. While Jonathan was passing through the woods during the war against the Philistines, he found honey dripping on the ground; he plunged his spear into it, and ate enough to restore his lost strength. He was, however, sentenced to death because he ate honey on a day of abstinence.

Honey was referred to in most ancient writings as a gift of God. St. Ambrose said: "The fruit of the Bees is desired of all, and is equally sweet to Kings and Beggars and it is not only pleasing but profitable and healthful, it sweetens their mouthes, cures their wounds and convaies remedies to inward Ulcers."

The Koran, the Code of Islam, recommended honey as a wholesome food and excellent medicine. In the XVIth Chapter of the Koran, entitled *The Bee*, we find: "There proceedeth from their bellies a liquor of various colour, wherein is medicine for men." The "various colour" refers to the diversified colors of honeys. Mohammed pronounced: "Honey is a remedy for all diseases." The Prophet ordered the eating of honey not only because it was an exquisite food and an important healing substance but because it brought one good luck. The followers of Islam looked upon honey as a talisman. The Mohammedans, to whom alcoholic fermented drinks were prohibited, drank their water with honey, which habit still prevails among the African Mohammedan negroes. Ismael Abulfeda, the thirteenth century historian, relates how Mohammed, on the day after his wedding to Safiya Hoya, a Jewess of Aaron's tribe, celebrated the occasion with a luxurious meal. Among the main delicacies, he mentions honey, dates and cream. When Mohammed reached the seventh heaven he found Christ, Who ordered Archangel Gabriel to offer Mohammed a cup filled with honey. The Mohammedan conception of Paradise was "rivers flowing with honey."

According to a Mohammedan legend, young Abraham (Aburam), who lived about 2000 B.C., spent fifteen months in a cave. On Allah's order, he obtained water from his thumb, milk from his index finger, honey from the middle one, date juice from the fourth, and butter from his little finger.

There is a story that a man once went to Mohammed and told him that his brother was afflicted with violent pains in his belly and with diarrhea, upon which the prophet bade him give his brother honey. He heeded the prophet's advice, but soon returned and reported to Mohammed that the medicine had not done his brother any good. Mohammed exclaimed: "Go and give him more honey, for God speaks true, and thy brother's belly lies." The dose being repeated, the man, by God's mercy and the salutary effect of honey, was cured. The Koran repeatedly mentions the technical skill of the bees in producing sweet honey from the bitter juices of plants. Mohammed maintained that medicines administered by physicians are bitter but those given by God are as sweet as honey. (The moderns believe that the more bitter the medicine the better the doctor.) An Arabic writer (Ibn Magih) quotes the words of the Prophet: "Honey is a medicine for the body and the Koran is medicine for the soul; benefit yourselves by the use of the Koran and of honey." The Arabs, before they ate honey, exclaimed: "Bism Allah" (in the name of Allah) or "Allah Akbar" (Allah the greatest). The Arabic name of the bee is *nahlat,* which means a gift— of course—of Allah, and *han* means honey. Apparently it was the root of the German "honig" and English "honey." Arabia was the last stepping stone before honey invaded Europe from the East.

Honey must have been abundant in ancient Egypt. The Hebrews referred to it as "a land flowing with milk and honey." The Egyptian papyri are full of praise about the curative properties of honey. The *Papyrus Ebers* especially praised its medicinal value. According to this most ancient source of knowledge, honey was not only a staple commodity but a popular medicine, extensively used internally, and also externally in surgical dressings for burns, ulcers and preeminently for weakness and inflammation of the eyes. Laxative and worm remedies of ancient Egypt without exception contained honey. Milk and honey was their choice for infant feeding. There were only a few medicines in ancient Egypt which did not contain honey. The bee, its producer, occupies a prominent place in all hieroglyphic writings. Most prescriptions of the papyri were taken to Greece and the Greeks introduced them to Europe where they are still used today.

In ancient China honey was used only as a component of diets and as a medicine. The Chinese never utilized honey as a sweetening substance. China is the native land of the sugar cane, and for this reason bees were rarely cultivated. Even today in the interior of China, honey can be obtained only in the old-style medicine shops.

In India, Persia, Arabia, Assyria, Greece and in the Roman Empire, honey was much in demand as a remedial agent for internal and external use. On the entire European Continent it was in popular use, especially among the Slavic and Nordic races. In the Eddas we find that the life of Liafsburg, the mother of Saint Lindgar, was saved with a spoonful of honey.

If we review the therapeutic field in which honey was used by the ancients, we find that its main employment was as a helpful remedy for gastric and intestinal disorders, especially as a pleasant laxative. Respiratory troubles were next in order. The sedative and soporific power of honey is often emphasized. The diuretic effect of honey was well known and it was a favored remedy for all kinds of inflammation of the kidneys, for gravel and stones. The antiseptic property of honey made it a desirable gargle, expectorant and a valuable adjunct in mouth hygiene. In inflammation of the eyes and eyelids honey was extensively used. Attic honey had a special reputation as a curative substance for eye disorders. The Egyptians carried its fame with them to their country. In one of the Egyptian papyri it is mentioned that a man begged that they fetch him some honey from Attica which he needed for his eyes. In surgical dressings and skin diseases it was a remedy of first choice. The smallpox patients were anointed with honey. It was also employed as a vehicle for nauseous or bitter medicines. Lucretius referred to it 2000 years ago:

> "Physician-like, who when a bitter draught
>   Of wormwood is disgusted by a child
>   To cheat his taste, he brims the nauseous cup
>   With the sweet lure of honey."

Hippocrates was a great believer in honey. He considered it a very good expectorant. According to Hippocrates, the physical virtues of honey were: "It causes heat, cleans sores and ulcers, softens hard ulcers of the lips, heals carbuncles and running sores." (Hippocrates alleged that if the seeds of cucumbers and other plants are first soaked in honey and then planted, "the fruit that groweth of them will taste sweeter.") He recommended honey for difficulty in breathing because "it causes spitting." Hippocrates believed that honey "with other things" is nourishing and induces a good complexion but eaten alone it attenuates rather than refreshes because it provokes urine and purges too much. According to the legend (Samuel Purchas, *A Theatre of Politicall Flying Insects*, 1657, p. 163), a swarm of bees lived for a long time in the sepulcher of Hippocrates, the prince of physicians, and produced honey there. Nurses carried children to the grave and anointed their lips with this magic honey which *easily* cured them. Dioscorides, the Greek physician (first century A.D.), whose *Materia Medica* is one of the oldest sources of medical knowledge, often mentions honey as an excellent medicine. He also praises the medicinal value of wax, propolis and honey-wine.

Cornelius Celsus remarked in *De Medicina* (first half of the first century A.D.) that a physician must heal in a safe, quick and pleasing manner (*tuto, cito et jucunde*), and all this could be best accomplished with honey.

Galen recommended the mixing of four parts of honey with one part of gall of the sea-tortoise which, when dropped into the eyes, would improve the sight. To quote Marcellus: "The honey pure and neat wherein the Bees are dead, let that drop into the eyes; or honey mixt with the ashes of the heads of Bees, makes the eyes very clear." Pliny also credited honey in which bees have died with the faculty of relieving dullness of sight and hearing. In antiquity, honey had a great reputation in producing clearer vision, which may be the reason for its reputation of endowing the power of divination, improving thus not only the physical but also the spiritual sight. Some historians believe that when Jeroboam sent his wife with a cruse of honey to the prophet Ahijah it was meant as a remedy for the prophet's blindness.

Honey and dead bees were used by Galen for growing hair. "Take Bees dead in combs, and when they are through dry make them into powder, mingle them with the honey in which they died and anoint the parts of the Head that are bald and thin-haired, and you shall see them grow again." The *Syriac Book of Medicines* recommends a handful of bees roasted in oil as a remedy to turn gray hair black. This ancient book of medical knowledge contains three hundred recipes in which honey is an important ingredient (over fifty of them contain wax).

Celsus recommended raw honey as a laxative and boiled honey as a cure for diarrhea. The reason, he thought, was because "the acrimony is taken away by boyling which wont to move the belly and to diminish the virtue of the food" (Libr. 3 C. 3). Galen recommended boiled and only seldom raw honey but forbids long or too intensive heating because this would make honey bitter. The Hindu physicians assumed that fresh honey was a laxative and honey which was over a year old, an astringent. Pliny burned the bees, mixed their ashes with honey and used the substance for all kinds of ailments: "Powdered bees with milk, wine or honey will surely cure dropsy, dissolve gravel and stones, will open all passages of urine and cure the stopping of the bladder. Bees pounded with honey cure griping of the belly." Muffet also had faith in honey with dead bees. "Honey wherein is found dead Bees is a very wholesome medicine, serving for all diseases." Aelian reported that honey from Pontus cured epilepsy.

Porphyry thought that honey had four excellent qualities: first, it is a nourishing food; second, a good cleanser; third, it has healing power; and fourth, it is pleasant on account of its sweetness. According to Aristoxenus (320 B.C.), anyone who eats honey, spring onions and bread for his daily breakfast will be free from all diseases throughout his lifetime. The ancient Hindus had great faith in the medicinal virtues and magic properties of honey, especially of aged honey. They used it mainly for coughs, pulmonary troubles, gastric and bilious disorders. The famous Arab physicians, such as El Madjoussy and El Basry, all spoke in laudatory terms of the curative power of honey and liberally used it in their professions for a variety of ailments. Arab physicians were reputed to cure tuberculosis with an extract made from the petals of roses and honey. The efficacy of this medicine was recognized for many centuries. Rosed honey is yet an official remedy in most modern pharmacopoeias. Paul of Aegina, Aetius, Oribasius were other honey enthusiasts.

The Koran recommended honey not only as a wholesome food, but as a useful diuretic, a laxative, an excellent remedy for various distempers, particularly those occasioned by phlegm, and also as a substance greatly assisting labor pains.

Norman Douglas describes in his *Paneros* the love-philters of antiquity and the value of honey in the preparations of amative elixirs. Besides honey, according to Douglas, the wings of bees have been used.

Honey was an important ingredient of all ancient satyriaca (*ad coitum irritantia tentaginem facientia*). The ancients had implicit faith in the power of honey to increase strength and virility. (The French consider not only honey but also the sting of the bee a powerful aphrodisiac.) The Hindu novices for priesthood had to abstain from meat, women, perfumes and . . . honey.

The ancients believed that people who fared freely on honey became more congenial and affectionate. They considered honey a cure for a sour disposition and bitter feelings. Pliny said: "All acrimony of the mind is pacified with sweet liquers, the spirits are made peaceable, the passages made softer and fitter for transpiration; and they are also good physick for manners." Pythagoras thought that body and soul function in harmony and that no food could be considered beneficial to one without being subservient to the other. He believed, for instance, that music was food for the soul and likewise conducive to good health. David played the harp before King Saul to cure his melancholy.

2. AS MEDICINE IN THE MIDDLE AGES

The population of the Middle Ages had great faith in honey. This is best illustrated by the statement of Charles Butler in the *History of Bees*, 1623: "Hoonni cleareth all the obstructions of the body, lossenth the belly, purgeth the foulness of the body and provoketh urine. It cutteth and casteth up Flegmatic matter and therefore sharpneth the stomachs of them, which by reason thereof have little appetite; it purgeth those things which hurt the clearness of the eyes and nourisheth very much. It breedeth good blood it sturreth up and preserveth natural heat and prolongeth old age; physicians do temper therewith such medicines as they mean keep long; yea the bodys of the dead, being enbalmed with Hoonni, have been thereby preserved from putrefaction. It is drunk against the biting of a Serpent or made Dog and it is good for them, which have eaten mushrooms or drunk Poppy; against which evil Rosed-hoonni is taken warm. It is also good for falling sickness and better than wine because it cannot arise to the head as wine doeth. Hoonni is most fit for old men, women and children, for such as rheumatic and flegmatic and generally for all that are of cold temperature. To young men and that of a hot constitution is not so good because it easily turned into kholer."

The climax of Butler's statement is "Hoonni is altered by distillation into a water which Raimundus Lullius (that excellent Kymist) called the Quintessence of Hoonni. This quintessence dissolveth gold and makes it potable; likewise any sort of precious stone that is put therein. It is of such virtue that if any be dying and drink two or three drams thereof, presently he will revive. If you wash any wound therewith, it will heal quickly. It is good also against cough, catarrh and pains of the melt and against many other diseases. It helpeth also falling sickness and preserveth the body from putrefaction. Of so marvellous efficacy is this water." Butler thought that honey "comforts and strengthens the stomach in the wise."

Samuel Purchas, pastor of Sutton, Essex (1657), claimed that it would require "a good day's work" to enumerate the worth and benefits of honey. Don Juan Manuel, from the royal house of Castile and Leon, the 13th century Spanish writer of stories, in his *El Conde Lucanor* still uses the old Spanish word *melezina* (mel=honey) instead of *medicina* (medicine).

Hieronymus Bock, in *Teutsche Speiszkammer,* Strassburg, 1539, made the same comments about honey as Charles Butler and both seem to quote the writings of Dioscorides (Libr. II), who believed that honey was best for weak and old people and for those of cold temperament. In young and "hot" people honey turns into gall. Old people obtain from honey good food and new blood. Dioscorides advocated the inhaling of honey for coughs, and its internal use as a good diuretic. Honey, he thought, was good for those who were poisoned by opium and mushrooms or were bitten by snakes and mad dogs. Dioscorides recommended that honey should be rubbed into the hair to kill lice and nits.

Jos. Roach, in *Parnassus medicinalis,* Ulm, 1663, eulogized honey in verses. For instance,

> "Der Honig treibt den Harn
> Und ist zur Lunge gut,
> Von Husten, Faulung auch
> Es stark bewahren tut."

(Honey drives the urine, is good to the lungs and a strong protector against cough and decay.)

An old English chronicle remarks: "Honey is still our chief sweetness, favorite salve and indispensable medicine."

(The German women for centuries had great faith in a

popular remedy called *Salvemet*, made from honey and
crushed bees. This was taken on St. Catherine's day and was
supposed to have a beautifying and strengthening effect,
besides regulating the menstrual flow.)

We find evidence in the folklore of almost all nations of
the faith the rural population had in the curative, even magic
power of honey. Youthful America is no exception. In the
Journal of American Folklore (II Vol.) there is an illustrative
tale told by an old woman. The story is about Mark Flaherty
who was riding home once after sunset when he heard a
voice behind him. Turning around, he could see no one.
Arriving home he heard the same mysterious voice but was
unable to trace its source. After retiring he could not sleep
and had a feeling that somebody was sitting on his chest.
Next morning he noticed that his hair had turned gray overnight. Towards evening he distinctly heard the same voice
again and noticed that a man was crawling in his direction.
Trying to nab the figure it vanished. Flaherty thereafter was
afraid to go out in the dark, became ill and emaciated.

A beggar called on him one day and when he learned of
his predicament advised him to get some honey and rub his
entire body with it. The bees suck the strength of flowers
which they mix with their own honey and that would cure
him, turn his hair dark again and his cheeks rosy. Flaherty
followed the suggestion and he fully recovered. He never
heard the weird voice again.

3. IN MODERN THERAPEUTICS

Honey plays an insignificant part in our modern *Materia
Medica*, though strained, clarified, borated and rose honey
are listed in many pharmacopoeias. The mel depuratum (clarified honey) is rather an inadequate substance because it is
subjected to heating and is filtered through cloth which also
robs it of some mineral elements.

In lay, let us call it unscientific medicine, especially in the
rural districts, however, honey is today a more popular nos-
trum than the medical profession would surmise. Physicians,
with few exceptions, grin broadly at the mere mention of the
medicinal and food merits of honey. Of course, the name
honey sounds rather homely, almost dilettante. How much
more knowledge and intelligence the term, cinchophen, for
example, reveals. This substance was widely advertised and

the medical fraternity, conformably, employed it. It soon became so popular that the general public began to use it indiscriminately. After it had caused irreparable harm and many patients had died from its effect, the sale without a prescription was prohibited. This is only one instance. On the other hand, people will ignore good things which are within their reach.

Something should be done to induce the medical profession to look more carefully into the remedial and dietetic value of honey. On the European continent, where physicians are paid for keeping patients in good health, honey is freely used. It is time that American physicians should do likewise and obviate the possibility of a rather embarrassing accusation that instead of preventing disease, they prevent health. It is the physician's duty to help and to educate the public.

In antiquity and all through the Middle Ages, honey was an important medicine. Up to the end of the last century, it still held the place of honor in the service of Aesculapius. Only with the advent of the millions of patented and well-advertised domestic and imported whatnots was honey almost banished as a curative substance, the same fate which it suffered as a sweetening matter upon the introduction of refined sugar. Thanks to the simple country-folk and to the primitive races, honey is yet in its glory as a dispenser of health and as a valued remedy. Honey cures were popular in many European countries for the tired feeling caused by the so-called spring fever.

The consideration alone that a snake is pictured coiled around the stick of Aesculapius, eager to feast from a cup of honey, ought to be sufficient exhortation to medical men to be more interested in this substance. (Aesculapius, the god of Medicine, who not only healed the sick but restored the dead to life, held the snake sacred. The snake was the emblem of health and recovery. The snakes were fed on honey or honey cakes. Whoever entered the cave of Trophonius had to throw honey cake to the snakes [Pausanias IX. 39:5]. Honey was also the favorite food of the fabled serpent, the guardian of the Acropolis [Herodot. VIII. 41]. The snake of Aesculapius in Cos was given honey and honey cake [Herondas IV. 90; Virgil *Aeneid* IV. 484].

Among the Asiatic races, including the Chinese and the Hindu, and among the Egyptians, Arabs and the African tribes, honey is still considered an excellent protective food and a sovereign internal and external remedy. Amongst the Wa-Sania tribes, British East Africa, a mother's only nutriment for several days after the birth of a child is honey with hot water. A boy, after he has been circumcised (usually at the age of 3 or 4) is permitted only to consume honey and water for a week. Among the Nandis some honey is placed on the tongue of a child before circumcision. Honey is often combined by them with the bark and leaves of certain trees and plants. Among the rural population of the old countries, especially among the Greeks, Italians, Hungarians and all the Slavic races, honey is a popular home remedy. Their laxative medicines, likewise those for coughs, bronchitis, tuberculosis and other pulmonary ailments, contain honey. For respiratory troubles honey is often mixed with anis, pepper, horseradish, ginger, mustard and garlic. A glassful of warm milk with a tablespoonful of honey is used for bronchitis and debilitated conditions. Goat's milk or buttermilk and honey is a favored and popular remedy for tuberculosis. Goat's milk is most nutritious and very digestible. It is nearest to human milk. There are more vitamins, minerals, fats and proteins in goat's milk than in any other milk. In the East, Far East, Africa and in most European countries goat's milk is extremely popular. Recently there have been considerable efforts made in the United States to popularize goat raising.

The diuretic effect of honey which was well known in antiquity, is still employed in kidney and bladder involvements. In pyelitis (inflammation of the renal pelvis) honey increases the amount of urine and exerts a decided antiseptic effect. The patients quickly improve; the urine clears and loses its putrid odor. The laxative effect of honey in these cases is also of advantage. One of the author's correspondents (J. L. McD., of Marion, Indiana), wrote thus about the subject: "A bee-keeping friend of mine suffered from tuberculosis of the kidney and was given up by two doctors fifteen years ago. He got to eating honey and plenty of it and he is today as peppy as a youngster." Honey is an important ingredient of worm-cures. The African tribes also mix their tobacco and their aphrodisiac remedies with honey.

Among the so-called "civilized" communities we find some people who favor honey, especially for throat and bronchial ailments. During many years' professional contact with opera singers, the writer has found that they frequently resorted to honey for the treatment of their throat affections. They consider it an excellent demulcent and expectorant. Three parts of honey and one part of compound tincture of benzoin is popular among singers; so is an occasional gulp from a mixture of two ounces of honey, one ounce of lemon juice and an ounce of pure glycerin. Honey (125 gm.) and alum (25 gm.) added to one quart of water is a useful gargle. The mixture of honey and alum is highly valued for sore throat and ulcerations of the gums and mouth. Hot milk and honey make an excellent remedy for husky throats.

Another correspondent of the author (M. S. of Kansas City, Mo.) has written about the curative value of honey in pulmonary affection, as follows: "In 1925, I became ill and consulted several doctors, all of whom gave the verdict of active tuberculosis. After seven months, two doctors gave me up, and said that my only chance was to go West, which I could not afford to do. At a later date, they frankly informed me that I had only three months to live and insisted on sending me to Colorado. I was then living in Kansas City, Missouri, and had previously been engaged in cement and paving work. I managed to land a job in Nemaha County, Kansas, about 140 miles west of Kansas City. My work was to establish an apiary of one hundred colonies for a commercial orchard. I was to 'batch' in a room in the apple house, which had a cement floor. Often it took all my strength to carry a gallon bucket of water from the well, one hundred feet away. In studying bees, I had learned the value of honey in driving out and destroying all germs in the human body. I used honey regularly and I worked to the limit of my strength. Three years later, the same doctors examined me and found only a few spots on my lungs. They absolutely refused to believe that I was the same person. Today, I take my place as an average man. I take care of two hundred fifty colonies of bees and a farm of twenty-five acres of land. The only help I have is about one month during the honey harvest. I don't know whether the honey cured me, or it was the fact that I was too lazy to crawl into my coffin, but I believe the honey and possibly the raw diet were the major factors of my recovery."

J. J. H., of Brownsville, Florida, reports that when his grandmother was a young girl she was given up by her physicians as a hopeless consumptive. Someone prescribed a diet of honey and goat's milk, with the result that she lived to the age of eighty-eight and was free from illness during the rest of her lifetime.

M. D. A., of Old Forge, New York, is certainly a great

admirer of honey. He writes: "Having kept bees and eaten honey for over thirty years, I can tell about my own experience and give also observations of other people who use honey exclusively for sweetening. I never have known a beekeeper who had any kind of kidney trouble. They all have a clear complexion, good eyesight and no lameness. Among my friends who eat honey and keep bees, there is no cancer or paralysis. My best remedy for a bee sting is to cover it with honey, even a deep burn will not scar if treated the same way. I have seen sour milk, whole wheat cracked for cereal, honey and butter do wonders in diet. I cured the cough of a great number of my friends, where other remedies failed, with this prescription:

>   4 tablespoonfuls of honey
>   1 teaspoonful of sulphur
>   5 drops of pure turpentine

Mix it, take half-teaspoonful two or three hours apart."

The soporific effect of honey is *par excellence*. The French Voirnot advocated it for insomnia. Dr. Lorand (of Carlsbad) also recommends honey as a good hypnotic and reconstructive. D. Dumoulin, when eighty years old, commented, "Chaque soir, avant de me mettre au lit, je prends une cuiller á cafe de miel, soit pur, soit dans du lait chaud, et je dors comme á vingt ans." (Every night, before I go to bed I take a teaspoonful of honey, sometimes pure, other times in hot milk and I sleep like when twenty years old.) A tumblerful of hot water with one or two tablespoonfuls of ripe honey and the juice of half a lemon has been the author's favorite potion for nervous insomnia. This simple and inexpensive home remedy has been greatly appreciated by his patients and most of them have assured him that it is more helpful than .... (an infinite number of patented drugs could equitably replace these dots).

In digestive disturbances honey is of great value. Honey does not ferment in the stomach because, being an inverted sugar, it is easily absorbed and there is no danger of a bacterial invasion. The flavor of honey excites the appetite and helps digestion. The *propoma* of the ancients, made of honey, was a popular appetizer. For anemics, dyspeptics, convalescents and the aged, honey is an excellent reconstructive and tonic. In malnutrition, no food or drug can equal it.

The laxative value of honey, on account of its lubricating effect, is well known. Its fatty acid content stimulates peristalsis. In gastric catarrh, hyperacidity, gastric and duodenal ulcers and gall bladder diseases honey is recommended by several eminent gastroenterologists.

Dr. Schacht, of Wiesbaden, claims to have cured many hopeless cases of gastric and intestinal ulcers with honey and without operations. It is rather unusual that a physician of standing has the courage and conviction to praise honey. The beekeepers and their friends know that honey will cure gastric and intestinal ulcerations, this distressing, prevalent and most dangerous malady, a precursor of cancer. But the news has not yet reached 99% of the medical profession. The remaining few physicians who know it, are afraid to suggest such an unscientific and plebeian remedy, for fear of being laughed at by their colleagues and scientifically inclined patients. You may read in almost every issue of apicultural papers the reports of correspondents regarding their experience with honey for gastric ulcers, after going through the medical *mill* for years without improvement, without even hope of ever getting cured. Then incidentally they meet a beekeeper or one of his converts and if they have courage and common sense (there are few) to heed the advice, they get well. It is disheartening for a physician to read such reports. For instance, a correspondent (A. L. T. of Omaha, Nebr.), writes in *Gleanings in Bee Culture,* February, 1931), "I have been a sufferer from ulcerated stomach for several years, part time in the hospital, part time in bed and nearly all the time in much pain. I noticed from the middle of September I was much better and gave no thought to the reason but kept up eating honey because I relished it. I had no attack since and it held good. . . ." It would fill a volume to assemble similar testimonials, praising particularly the curative value of honey in gastric and intestinal disorders, including ulcers. Father Kneipp, a great admirer of honey, remarked: "Smaller ulcers in the stomach are quickly contracted, broken and healed by it."

Honey is a rapidly acting source of muscular energy and has great value as a restorative. The protoplasm craves sugar as does an individual. Muscles in action consume three and a half times as much glycogen as when at rest. A normal heart, according to Starling, uses glycogen at the rate of four milligrams per gram of heart per hour. The invigorating effect of honey was discussed under the heading, "Honey for Athletes and Soldiers." It is not surprising that many well-known physicians recommend honey for an ailing heart. Dr. Lorand in *Old Age Deferred*, and in *Life Shortening Habits and Rejuvenation*, expresses his faith in honey as a *sine qua non* in arteriosclerosis and weak heart. Dr. G. N. W. Thomas, of Edinburgh, Scotland, in an article in the *Lancet* remarks that "in heart weakness I have found honey to have a marked effect in reviving the heart action and keeping patients alive. I had further evidence of this in a recent case of pneumonia. The patient consumed two pounds of honey during the illness; there was an early crisis with no subsequent rise of temperature and an exceptionally good pulse. I suggest that honey should be given for general physical repair and, above all, for heart failure." Sir Arbuthnot Lane also emphasized the value of honey as a heart and muscle stimulant, and as an excellent source of energy. There is no better food, he thought, to meet muscular fatigue and exhaustion.

Carbohydrate and especially sugar metabolism has great importance. Energy is primarily the result of carbohydrate assimilation. Hyperglycemic individuals are, as a rule, more energetic and less prone to fatigue; subglycemic people tire easily and are apathetic. Certain nervous types, though glycophile subjects, exhaust their sugar reserve fast and wear out just as quickly. Lack of energy is not always due to laziness.

In typhoid fever and pneumonia, where the digestive functions are badly crippled, honey is most beneficial. Why embarrass enfeebled digestions with foods which require chemical changes before their assimilation when we can administer a serviceable and pleasant food which is predigested? For the treatment of typhoid fever, honey diluted in water is the author's preferential food. It is an ideal substance, in this special instance, on account of its demulcent effect on the inflamed intestines, its rapid assimilation and its capability to supply food and energy without causing fermentation, which is so much feared in typhoid fever. Honey, a concentrated and predigested food, is absorbed orally 100% and per rectum 96%. For rectal feeding honey is exceptionally well adapted. Galen's honey and oil enema was highly valued in antiquity. While sugar favors worms, honey was considered as one of the best vermifuge remedies by all ancients and it is widely used for this purpose, even today, by primitive races.

Medical textbooks pay only little attention to the real

worth and merit of honey. The results which some physicians have derived from the use of honey, as a rule, have been incidental. Dr. C. H. English, Medical Director of the Lincoln National Life Insurance Co., vividly describes his own experience (*Gleanings in Bee Culture*, 55:1927). About forty-one years ago the doctor practiced medicine among rural folk. He acquired two colonies of bees which soon increased and it was not long until he had more honey on hand than he and his family could use. Not wishing to sell honey, it occurred to him to distribute his surplus stock among patients. There were a sufficient number of cases which offered an excellent field to try out the nutrimental, medicinal and tonic effects of honey. In respiratory troubles, the doctor found that honey acted not only as a good expectorant but as a valuable heart tonic. In pneumonia, near the crisis, when honey was freely given, it had a marked effect. The benefits were so evident that the administration of honey became a routine practice with him. He found no other food or heart stimulant which had a more lasting effect. This practice he kept up for fifteen years with the most gratifying results. Occasionally in severe cases, when he ran short of honey, he noticed the difference and when he succeeded again in procuring some the improvement was quite manifest. Dr. English also used honey successfully in infant feeding.

The blood reconstructive power of honey can be surmised from a recent report from Germany. According to this information Edmund Eckardt (thirty-five years old) a champion blood donor, whose only visible means of support is to supply blood for transfusions, just celebrated his jubilee. He has saved fifty lives in the last three years. When interviewed as to how he makes good his losses he described his diet. During daily breakfast he consumes honey; for luncheon he has fish and vegetables and drinks orange juice with his dinner. His main reliance is on honey and oranges, of which he eats thirty a day. An expert of the Blood Transfusion Betterment Association of New York, when interviewed on the subject, suggested that Eckhardt's faith in oranges is unjustified because what a blood donor needs is iron, and Eckardt in fact, "does not mention that any part of his diet contains iron." Another occasion where "dethroned" honey was utterly disregarded! Count Luckner, of World War fame, is an extremely moderate eater. He is about sixty-five years old and looks no more than forty. Luckner bends a silver half-dollar

with two fingers and tears a Manhattan telephone directory
into small pieces with greatest ease. The Count relates that
his first food in the morning is a "goodly portion of honey."

Many people, especially beekeepers, and a few physicians
(this writer among them) claim that honey taken internally
prevents and often cures arthritic and rheumatoid ailments.
The peasants of Hungary even put a honey poultice over the
big toe in gout and they say the pain disappears in half an
hour. Such assertions have, of course, all the earmarks of
unscientific broach. Still there are many who insist that
honey has benefited them more than all the "scientific" vac-
cines. Vitamin C deficiency would explain an impaired circu-
lation and recent researches (James F. Reinhart, Studies
relating to Vitamin C deficiency in rheumatic fever and rheumatoid arthritis, *Annals of Internal Medicine*, December,
1935) clearly prove that lack of vitamin C favors the development of infectious arthritis. Dr. Heermann of Kassel, Germany, suggests (*Fortschritte der Medizin*, Vol. 54, 1936) the
use of honey for rheumatism, atrophy of muscles, nervous
conditions, tuberculotic glands, etc., both internally and externally. He employed honey with success for thirty-five
years. Dr. Heermann thinks it is unnecessary to extract the
venom of the bees to treat these conditions. Honey itself
contains some venom because the bees use their stings not
only for defense but also for the preservation of honey.

Many beekeepers are of the opinion that, besides the admitted and generally recognized curative effects of the stings
in rheumatic ailments, honey also contributes its benefits in
preventing and curing these diseases. As an illustration, I
quote a letter from J. L. McD., of Marion, Indiana: "I began
beekeeping because I had rheumatism, and it has disappeared, but I consider it due more to the fact that I ate
honey than to bee stings. Nearly four years ago, I had rheumatism in my knees. I finally went to Dr. K. ...., of
Marion, Indiana, for advice. He put me on a citrous fruit
diet, allowing only honey. In a week, he allowed breakfast
food sweetened with honey. It did the work, and I liked
honey so well that I bought a few hives of bees to supply my
family, and now—nearly four years later—I want everyone
to know honey and to like it, as Nature's own health-sweet,
full of pep and vitamins that God gave us, pure as snow. My
growing son is developing into a healthy, sturdy ten-year old
since the use of honey, egg and milk drinks. My rheumatism
never returned."

Honey, taken by itself and not mixed with other foods, was considered by the ancients an excellent remedy for obesity. Beekeepers today, who know it from their own experience, will confirm this allegation. The regimen, at a glance, sounds rather unscientific to a modern physician; nevertheless it has a deeper biochemical meaning than it appears to have. Fats and sugars are both carbon-containing and energy-providing foods which burn up by contact with oxygen and create energy. Sugars which contain more carbon elements and are more inflammable produce energy more quickly. Fats which contain less carbon and oxygen than sugars, are utilized slower because their purpose is only to supply reserve energy; they require more oxygen and more draught to set them afire and are not meant for immediate use. If there is not enough sugar to keep the fires burning, the system will resort to its reserve fat. Accordingly when sugars, especially honey, are ingested into the system they will cause a rapid combustion and the fats will burn with the aid of the draught produced by their "fire." If an organism is slow to burn up fat (as in obesity), it will be assisted by the rapidity of sugar metabolism. The process could be compared to setting slowly inflammable coal ablaze with the aid of straw, kindling wood or even oil. Of course, there is sufficient oxygen in carbohydrates to assist in the combustion of carbon elements even without an outside source of oxygen.

Acknowledging some more medical information received from the laity, the writer's attention has been repeatedly called to the beneficial effect of honey on hay fever victims. There are many reports that the consumption of honey collected by bees from goldenrod and fireweed will cure hay fever superinduced by the selfsame pollen. Now comes Dr. George D. McGrew, of the Army Medical Corps of the William Beaumont General Hospital in El Paso, Texas, with a statement in an article published in the *Military Surgeon* that during the 1936 hay-fever season thirty-three hay-fever sufferers obtained partial or complete relief through the consumption of honey, produced in their vicinity. The brood cells contain a considerable amount of bee-bread (pollen) stored by the bees for their young and when this is orally administered it will produce a gradual immunity against the allergic symptoms caused by the same pollen. Dr. McGrew found particular relief for patients when they chewed the honey with the wax of the brood-cells. The hospital staff also made an alcoholic extract from pollen and administered it in from one to ten drop doses, according to the requirements of the patients.

Old beekeepers will tell you that a glassful of hot water with a tablespoonful of honey and some lemon juice will cure influenza and also help the pocketbook. (We physicians should not begrudge the medical propensity of farmers. They seem to agree with Bernard Shaw's remark that every profession is a conspiracy against the laity, so they retaliate. And the time-honored principle, experience versus theory, upon which Napoleon so often commented, should also be taken into consideration. The Hungarians have liberally consumed paprika for a thousand years and are convinced that it has contributed in a great measure to their health and temperament. After Professor Szent-Györgyi, the discoverer of Vitamin C, had tried unsuccessfully in Chicago to produce this vitamin from tons of liver, he returned very much disappointed to Hungary, where he accidentally found that red pepper is a rich source of Vitamin C.)

Honey would have a wider and better use in modern medicine if comprehensive microchemical and physiological studies would be instituted to determine the types of honey which are best suited to particular cases. The properties and tendencies of honeys vary according to the chemical characteristics of the nectar and pollen of plants from which they were collected. Dr. C. A. Browne, Principal Chemist in charge of research, Bureau of Chemistry and Soils, U.S. Department of Agriculture, admits that the gross composition of honeys of various types have been accurately determined but that comparatively little has been done and much more remains to be done toward ascertaining the nature and quantities of less common substances that occur in honey. Nitrogenous compounds (proteins), though honey contains these in small amounts, still play a very important rôle in the utilization of honey. The same applies to amino acids, various colloidal substances, to the mineral constituents and enzymes which honey contains. We have comparatively little definite knowledge about the so-called dextrins. The mineral content of honey considerably affects the degree of its acidity (pH). Dr. Browne thinks that more knowledge on the subject would be of great value in earmarking the various types of honey, which would serve as a guide in choosing the most suitable types for particular use.

HONEY AND DIABETES

Diabetes is a fundamental disorder of metabolism, primarily that of carbohydrates. It is due to a deficiency of the pancreas, a gland connected with the alimentary canal which, under the circumstances, does not produce sufficient insulin. It is a weakness or exhaustion of the gland. In diabetes the ingested carbohydrates, sugars and starches cannot be utilized, but are eliminated in the urine. Part of the food turns into sugar and the glutton has to return to Nature his illegitimate gains. The victim must famish in the midst of plenty. It is really a revenge of Nature. Lean people rarely acquire diabetes. In obese subjects the excess sugar and starch which they consume does not sufficiently oxidize, but forms fat which is already a disintegration of the organism.

A word should be said regarding the cause of diabetes. Most medical textbooks carefully avoid even mentioning the subject. Others acknowledge that the cause of diabetes is unknown. The author's personal comprehension is that the abuse of artificial sugar and salt are mainly to be blamed for it by producing an inflammation or sclerosis of the pancreas. The influence of white sugar already has been discussed. With regard to salt, he would set forth that animal diabetes is confined to horses, cattle and dogs. Salt is given to horses (occasionally also sugar) and to cattle, mixed in their fodder, and dogs obtain it in our waste food.

R. Arima of Tokyo, Japan, Director of the Arima Institute, experimented on himself. He had never had any diabetic ailment. In 1934, at the age of fifty-three he purposely consumed an excess of salt with the result that he suffered from excessive urine secretion, followed by diabetes. He repeated the experiment twice with the same result. He thought that diabetes could be easily cured by the limited use of, or total abstinence from salt. Arima quotes a noted authority who made the statement that civilized man is "pickled" in salt. In his opinion even hardening of the arteries and premature senility is caused by salt. A friend of the late John D. Rockefeller related to this author that during a dinner the old gentleman warned him never to use salt because the substance is injurious to health. As Mr. Rockefeller almost reached the class of centenarians his admonition is worthy of consideration.

Vegetarians and herbivorous animals crave salt because

they require it. Fruits, vegetables and plants, in general, contain ample other minerals but are insufficient in sodium chloride. Meat eaters can get along without salt. Many teachers of nutrition are against the use of salt. They claim that an excess of it will produce rigidity and inactivity. The brain, heart, arteries, muscles, salivary glands, eyes and sex organs lose their elasticity, become indurated and finally ossified. Lime, which commercial sugars contain, has a similar effect. When the biological chemists will use more commonsense than microscopes they will also establish the fact that refined sugars contribute more to the prevalanece of arthritis than has so far been surmised.

It is much beyond the scope of this review to enumerate the ill effects of diabetes. One of the cardinal troubles is lack of glycogen (animal starch) which is normally deposited in the muscles, of course, the heart, the blood and mainly in the liver (the savings bank of glucose), where it is stored and later utilized as the most important energy-producing substance of the organism. Normal blood contains about 0.10% glucose.

If a diabetic organism is unable to oxidize glucose, it will have vital effect also on other processes of metabolism, mainly on the metabolism of fat. The burning of carbohydrates, especially glucose, is indispensable for the burning of fat. Fats burn in the flame of carbohydrates. Imperfect oxidation of fats produces the formation of unoxidized fatty acids, commonly called acetone bodies, which will disturb the acid-base equilibrium of the system and finally will deplete the entire alkali reserve of the body.

The importance of sugar metabolism on the spinal column and brain is evident. The blood of the veins which leaves the brain contains less sugar and more acids than the blood of the arteries which centers upon it. Sugar assimilation has an important function in the chemical activities of brain cells. The successful therapeutic application of insulin in various mental disorders clearly demonstrates this. The lack of sugar assimilation of a diabetic, the accompanying depression, comatose states, even fatal ending, prove the vital importance of sugar metabolism on the activities of the brain cells.

The administration of insulin, a pancreatic hormone, corrects the pathological condition in diabetes and converts the carbohydrates into glycogen, which a diabetic constitution is unable to perform. Insulin is an adjunct in the treatment of diabetes but by no means a cure. The use of insulin is a burdensome procedure. The patient must inject insulin about half an hour before each meal to effectuate this function. Its dosage must first be determined because the units of insulin must correspond with the subsequent meal, with the patient's sugar tolerance, etc. The patient's individual response and also the amount of carbohydrates must be rigorously controlled and frequently modified. It is a tedious performance involving considerable time and expense, besides anxiety, and a careful application of complex chemistry and mathematics.

Any substance which could be utilized in mild diabetic cases to convert carbohydrates, by oral administration, into glycogen would be invaluable and far exceed in usefulness the dominant but otherwise beneficial insulin. The relinquishment of the cumbersome self-administered hypodermic injections alone would be of inestimable service.

Whether diabetics could utilize honey by converting it into glycogen to supply a much-needed source of energy for their depleted systems is an issue worth a thorough and *unbiased* investigation. There are many indications that there is more than a possibility of using honey for these sufferers.

Honey and refined sugars greatly differ not only in chemical characteristics but also in physiological effects. The circumstance alone that honey contains invert sugars and saves the debilitated alimentary organs the additional labor of inverting commercial sugars, is an important factor and of considerable advantage.

In relationship to diabetes there are also other distinctly heterogenous features in sugar and honey. If insulin were administered to a diabetic patient before a meal and the insulin units were in excess of the consequently consumed carbohydrates, or there was no food given at all, a severe, often disastrous insulin-shock would supervene. The reason for this occurrence is that the insulin will digest and consume the already scanty sugar reserve of the organism and an undersupply of blood-sugar (subglycemia) is just as dangerous as an oversupply (hyperglycemia). The only way to correct such a contingency is to administer a sufficient amount of glucose to compensate the action of excess insulin.

Cases have been reported where a liberal amount of honey was administered to avert an insulin shock due to subglycemia, but it was of no benefit; on the other hand, a subsequent administration of glucose rapidly neutralized the harm-

ful effects of insulin. The slow absorption of levulose and the
delay of transforming it in the system into glucose would
account for the inefficiency. This plainly proves that a fundamental chemical and physiological contrast exists between
ordinary sugar and honey. There is much the same disparity
between glucose and levulose, the latter an important component of honey. The symptoms of subglycemia which follow
the complete removal of the liver in animals are promptly
dispelled by the administration of glucose, while levulose is
ineffective. It is noteworthy that levulose is rarely, if ever,
found in the blood.

Diabetic patients who have had to endure for endless years
the self-inflicted injections of insulin are often exposed to
insulin-shock, which is really subglycemic reaction. Sometimes it is impossible to give an adequate reason for this
dangerous and occasionally fatal occurrence. There are many
causes which may produce such a state and diabetics ought
to be well instructed in their appreciation. This is a difficult
task for a layman, often enough even for an intelligent physician. The most common causes which are responsible for
such a state are, as a rule, errors in administering the proper
amount of insulin, usually too large a dose; a delay in eating
an appropriate meal; that is, a poor adjustment of diet or loss
of part of the food by vomiting, diarrhea or gastric obstruc-
tion; violent exercise in combination with insulin, etc. Diabetics often use the same site for injections. This delays or
prevents absorption and requires an increase of insulin, which
additional dose, if injected into a new site, will absorb rapidly, lower the blood-sugar level and produce a shock.

Many instances have been reported where honey was well
tolerated by diabetics and supplied them with required energy. In 1933, after the author had published a questionnaire
to beekeepers through the courtesy of apicultural journals, to
obtain information about the effects of bee stings, especially
about their remedial value in rheumatic and arthritic conditions, many correspondents volunteered illuminating reports
about the medicinal value of honey. Some of these communi-
cations state that honey has been used by them in hopeless
diabetic conditions with the best success and resulted in
cures. Some reports are very instructive. Mr. G. J., of Kau-
kauna, Wisconsin, writes, "I am a railroad engineer by trade,
but I became a diabetes victim and I had to resign my job
because I fell away to nothing. The doctors gave me up and

proclaimed that there was no hope for me. Then I made up my mind to take up a diet that I asked for but the doctors refused and here it is:

Spinach, raw or cooked, mostly raw.
Lettuce, sweetened with honey and lime juice.
Raw carrots, washed, brushed and grated, sweetened with honey to taste.
Raw cabbage salad with lime juice and honey.
Ripe tomatoes, raw or canned, sweetened with honey.
Whole wheat bread.

"Began this diet in 1922 and at the end of 1923 the doctors could not find a trace of sugar, though several of them have tested me to satisfy their curiosity. I am now past 65, eat anything on the table, and will do as much work as any man of my age, if not more, after going through two railroad wrecks and being picked up twice for dead. Whisky was not the cause of the wrecks, for I do not touch the cursed stuff."

Mr. L. M. D. of Edmeston, New York, writes that he not only cured many cases of rheumatism with bee stings but also supplies a list of people who were victims of diabetes. After they indulged in honey they recovered. "Mr. and Mrs. F. D. both suffered from diabetes, doctoring with various physicians for a long time without improving. Finally they went on a diet consisting of large amounts of honey and plenty of fruit, and today both are alright."

Such disclosures (call them intrusions), even though they originate from the laity, ought to arouse the attention of the venerable medical fraternity.

To justify the supposition that honey can be given to diabetics, there are also statements from members of the medical profession. Dr. F. C. Ameiss advocated tupelo honey for diabetics, as having a minimum percentage of dextrose and a maximum of levulose. (Tupelo is a tree of the dogwood family.) Dr. Desiderius de Beszedits, of Coyuca de Catalan, Guerrero, Mexico, in an article in the *Medical World*, October, 1934, "Treatment of Diabetes," wrote the following: "Just one more thing to conclude: the employing of honey-diet in the treatment of diabetes may look antiscientific, antimedical, even rather silly to the theoretical minded, uninitiated or to a superficial observer. Just at this writing, my bee flocks (a cross between the lazy native Indian wasp-like bee and the large, ever-busy Hungarian—also called Italian—bee, I imported from Europe) are busy gathering honey from a plant now in bloom here, called retama or tecoma mollis, retania or tronadora. We make tincture and fluid extract of this plant (leaves and roots), and I give it to diabetic patients in drop doses in manzanilla tea when I cannot obtain the leaves for the tea that I use in preference. The tea, the tincture and the fluid extract of this plant have a decidedly and markedly antiglycosuric and eupeptic quality and its antipolyuric effect is notably rapid. Now we all know that the bee sucks the quintessence of the flower juice, adds something of her own to it (saliva or some other substance) and so manufactures it into honey. Each country has a large number of provenly medicinal plants, and the bees gather their honey from such flowers. Making our deductions, it is not difficult to understand why, on this basis, honey fits into the curative diet for diabetes. Most likely it is just the proper food for the depleted hungry glands." (The belief that the curative properties of certain plants are transmitted by the bees from the blooms into the honey they produce, is rather widespread. Menelik, the great King of the Ethiopians, according to Dr. Theodorows [*Lancet*, 1897] grew Coso trees under which he placed the hives. The Coso honey which the bees gathered from the blooms was considered an excellent worm remedy. A tablespoonful of honey in water was supposed to be sufficient to produce results. The natives of India drop lotus honey into the eyes to cure cataracts. The belief in the anti-tuberculotic effect of Eucalyptus honey is world-wide.)

Dr. A. Y. Davidov of Russia has found honey a good substitute for sugar and other sweet foodstuffs in diabetes. Dr. Davidov believes that honey prevents acetonemia and diminishes the amount of sugar in the urine in spite of the fact that honey contains 75% sugar. One of his patients used one pound of honey in ten days without an increase of the sugar rate in the urine. When the use of honey was stopped for a while the sugar percentage in the urine rose and the patient was again given four teaspoonfuls of honey daily, after which the sugar rate again dropped. Dr. Davidov reported six more instances where honey had a beneficial effect in diabetes.

Dr. L. R. Emerick of Eaton, Ohio, a specialist in diabetes, used honey in the diet of more than 250 diabetic patients with success. The fame of the late Dr. R. J. Goss of Middlebury, Vermont, was proclaimed throughout the State for helping diabetics on a honey diet. A neighbor of his related that he has seen many patients arrive for treatments weak and emaciated but they soon gained in weight, looked splendid and were able to walk for miles.

(The author would earnestly caution diabetics not to use honey without the advice and strict control of their physicians.)

Professor A. Szent-Györgyi, the discoverer of Vitamin C, published interesting results which he obtained by peroral administration of succinic acid in the treatment of acidosis of diabetics (*Orvosi Hetilap.* Budapest, No. 24, June 12, 1937). These, if confirmed, may explain the beneficial effects of various acids, among others lactic, succinic, citric, malic acid, etc., which honey contains. The formation of dangerous acetone in diabetes is possibly corrected through the aid of these acids.

HEATHER HONEY

Magic healing power was attributed to heather, this modest little wild flower of the Scottish Highlands, so dear to the heart of all Scotsmen. The legendary lore and lay connected with this favorite mountain bloom, the emblem of solitude, was shared by the honey which the bees extracted from it. Heather designates a flower of the heath (in German, *heide*) and its connection with the word heathen, pagan (in German, *heide* also means pagan) reflects a quaint superstition. Both in Scotland and in Germany a belief existed that the heather grew from the blood of a heathen. In Scotland, on Halloween, the witches are supposed to ride on heather brooms.

The heather flower is purplish, suggesting the color of blood. White heather is extremely rare and it is supposed to bring good luck, not unlike a four-leaf clover. Queen Victoria mentioned in a letter that when she was a young bride and was driving fast to Balmoral Castle, her coachman suddenly jumped off the carriage to pick a white heather for which "he had an extraordinary eye to find," and remarked that "a Highlander would never pass one without picking it, because it is considered to bring one good fortune."

The nectar which heather blooms contain is rich in minerals. The Picts had the secret of making excellent ale from the "tender tops of the twigs." Heather ale was called heather-crop, meaning the top of the plant. Robert Louis Stevenson refers to heather ale in *A Galloway Legend:*

> From the bonny bells of heather
>   They brewed a drink lang-syne,
> Was sweeter far than honey,
>   Was stronger far than wine.
> They brewed it and they drank it,
>   And lay in blessed swound
> For days and days together
>   In their dwellings underground.

Leyden also refers to it in *The Heather:*

> For once thy mantling juice was seen to laugh
> In pearly cups, which monarchs loved to quaff;

Heather ale was much used among the Picts; but when that nation was extirpated by the Scots the secret of making it perished with them.

We know the legend relating how anxious were the Scots to learn the secret of the strength-giving heather ale. When the last two living members of the Picts, father and son, were brought before Kenneth the Conqueror, he offered them their life on condition that they reveal the method of heath-liquor making. After they refused Kenneth ordered the son to be killed. The father was still obdurate but his life was spared and he was imprisoned. He lived much beyond the limits of mortal existence but became blind and bed-ridden. Once he overheard some young men boasting of their strength. He felt their wrists, remarking that they were not feeble but their vigor could not be compared to men who drank heather ale. He asked for an iron bar and broke it with his hands. It was an old Scotch saying that mead-drinkers have as much strength as meat-eaters.

The medicinal properties of heather had a wide repute in antiquity. Parkinson in his *Theatrum Botanicum*, 1640 A.D., remarks: "It hath a digesting quality, resolving the malignity of humors, by transpiration or sweating; which a decoction of the flowers being drunke, doth perform, and thereby giveth much ease to the paines within the body, and expelleth the worms therein also, the leaves and flowers made into a decoction is good against the stings or bitings of serpents and other venomous creatures; and the same being drunke warm, for thirty days together, morning and evening, doth absolutely breake the stone and drive it forth; the same, also, or the destilled water of the whole plant, being drunke easeth the chollicke; the said water or the juyce of the herbe dropped into the eyes helpeth the weaknesse of the sight."

A decoction of heather "with faire water to be drunken warm both morning and evening in the quantity of five ounces three hours before meat, against the stone in the bladder; but at last the patient must enter into a bath made of the decoction and whiles he is in the said bath, he must sit upon some of the heather that made the foresaid bath. By the use of bath, dyet and decotion hee has knowne many to be holpen, so that the stone has come from them in very small pieces." Dioscorides' highly-praised Erica plant was undoubtedly heather.

The same curative power which was imputed to the plant was also attributed to heather honey. Rev. Hugh Macmillan remarked that "Mount Hybla itself could not boast of more luscious honey than the liquid amber which the bees gathered from the heather-bells." The Scotch thought that heather honey had a "grousey" taste.

Heather honey has world-wide repute as a specific remedy for many ailments. It is in great demand in foreign countries and is sold at a premium. Dr. Barton, during his stay in Edinburgh, noticed the distinct soporific effect of heath-honey. It is often so thick that it can not be readily separated from the combs by centrifugal force unless kept in a warm place for several days before extracting.

Pure heather (ling) honey does not granulate unless 10 per cent of pollen grains of other plants are present. (But 5 per cent of charlock might start granulation.) It is of a jelly consistency with a multitude of tiny air bubbles which give a characteristic sparkle. If the honey is heated these bubbles rise to the surface and their absence at once reduces the merit of the honey. In common parlance, pure heather honey does not imply absolute purity. If there is 20 per cent of other pollen present, it would still be reckoned good heather honey; and even if it had upwards of 40 per cent of foreign pollen grains, that honey might, by flavor, aroma and consistency, pass anywhere as good heather honey. Bell heather (Erica) does granulate, and it is to be classed with other dark honeys; for it has not the characteristic color, sparkle, consistency, astringency, flavor, and pollen of the genuine heather honey (John Beveridge, President of the Scottish Beekeepers' Association).

EUCALYPTUS HONEY

The cultivation of Eucalyptus trees in malaria-infested regions proved to be instrumental in eradicating this dreadful disease. In certain parts of Australia, malaria entirely disappeared after these fast growing *fever-trees* had been planted. Important medicinal values were always attributed to the sap of these trees. Their blooms are rich in pollen and nectar.

The Trappist monastery of *Tre Fontane*, near Rome, was built by the monks on soil which was infested with malaria. (The name originated from the legend which relates that when St. Paul was decapitated there by a powerful blow, his head rolled along with great force and from three places, where it touched the ground, wells issued.) After the monks had planted forests of Eucalyptus trees, the region became habitable. The Trappist monks conduct extensive apiaries there with two honey harvests, in May and in October. Some hives produce yearly as much as 120 pounds of honey (H. Reepen). On account of the considerable demand, Eucalyptus honey is high-priced and it affords a fair income to the priests.

Eucalyptus honey is dark in color, with a rather unpleasant taste and a strong aromatic odor. Australia supplies the largest part of the demand. In Germany they pay three to four marks a pound for such imported honeys. Dr. Ullersberger of Strassburg thought that genuine Eucalpytus honey is an unparalleled substance; it is strengthening, blood-forming, blood-purifying, nourishing, and besides, produces appetite. He advised adding, on account of its reconstructive power, one to three tablespoonfuls to any diet.

The Trappist *Liqueur de Tre Fontane* is also popular. The monks prepare the extract, with the aid of the most modern distilling apparatus, from the leaves of the Eucalyptus trees.

CHAPTER XII

HONEY IN SURGERY

Honey has a distinct bactericidal power which is mainly due to its hygroscopic property. All living organisms require a certain amount of moisture to maintain their lives. When bacteria come in contact with honey they are deprived of the vital moisture and perish. The acid reaction of honey also renders it an unfavorable medium for the bacteria to grow in. Most microorganisms which affect the human body are destroyed in honey.

Honey applied to ulcerated surfaces has a unique function. Soon after its application a profuse and intense centrifugal flow of lymph is noticeable and the entire torpid surface of the wound becomes soaked in fluid. This leucocytic lymph collection which honey produces has not only a bactericidal power but the rinsing function of the free-flowing liquid will greatly contribute to the cleansing of the wounds and will stimulate and promote granulation and healing. The ancient Greeks often refer to "epomphalia," a navel ointment made from honey for the newborn. Old mead, which is almost as extinct today as the dodo, was also used as an antiseptic lotion.

The external application of honey has an age-old history. The ancient Egyptians used it as a surgical dressing. The Papyrus Ebers recommended that wounds be covered for four days with linen dipped in honey and incense. They believed that cataracts yielded to treatments with honey. Honey dropped into the eyes was supposed to have cured inflammations and other ailments of the eyelids. To quote the amusing report of Vigerius: "I have cured a Horse stone blind with Honey and Salt and a little crock of a pot mixed. In less than three daies, it hath eaten off a tough filme, and the Horse never complained after." In the July, 1937 issue of the *American Bee Journal* (page 350) "A Subscriber" from New York State writes as follows: "I had a horse going blind with a white film over his eye which seemed to hurt. His eye was shut and watered. I dipped white honey into his eye with a feather for several nights. In a day or so the film was gone and the eye looked bright and good."

The Chinese and Hindus cover the entire bodies of their smallpox patients with honey to hasten the termination of the disease and also to prevent the formation of scars. Galen thought that "Hony warmes and cleares Wounds and Ulcers, attenuates and discusseth excrescencies in any part of the body." The Talmud recommended honey for ulcerated wounds, especially for extensive sores of animals. *Ceromel*, made with one part of wax and four parts of honey, is popular in the tropics for ulcers because it never becomes rancid.

During the Middle Ages honey was extensively used in the form of ointments and plasters for boils, wounds, burns and ulcers, plain or mixed with other ingredients. Charles Butler thought that honey "will knit together hollow and crooked ulcers and likewise close other disjoyned flesh." He highly praised the *Unguentum Aegyptiacum* which was made by boiling honey, vinegar and wintergreen. This plaster, according to Butler, would "open, clean, dry and digest all inflammations and resist putrefaction." Rectal suppositories contained honey and wax. Galen's honey and oil enema was popular for centuries.

Richard Remnant (*The History of Bees*, London, 1637) had implicit faith in "admirable baths made of honey which are excellent for Aches and strong Itches." A friend of his had "a foul itch that he was like a Leper." He cured him in the following manner: He used an empty Wine cask, called a Pipe, and "took out one head" and made a liquor of water and honey, making it pretty strong with honey and "heated it as hot as he could endure to stand in it," and poured it into the Pipe and "caused him to stand in it up to his neck a pretty while." This he did "three days, one after another, and he recovered as clear as ever." He had a like experience with "divers Aches." "If it be renewed every day with a little honey, it will be better."

The rural populations of the European continent, especially that of the Slavic countries, used honey for all kinds of wounds and inflammations. "Honey ointment," consisting of equal portions of honey and white flour, well mixed with a little water, had a wide usage. A good ointment should be more solidified than too liquid. Honey and burnt alum was another popular combination. In croupous diphtheria it was the accepted method of mothers to grip with their fingers a chunk of honey and vigorously rub, as far as they could reach, the throat and air passages of the patients. A honey poultice was also applied around the neck. Several drops of warm honey in the ears was considered an excellent remedy for pain, inflammation and ringing of the ear. Galen remarked: "Hony infused warme by itself wonderfully helps exulcerated ears, especially if they cast forth ill flavours, as also their singings and inflammations." Marcellus Empyricus suggested: "Honey, Butter and Oyle of Roses, of each a like quantity, warme, helps the paine of the ears, dulness of the sight and the white spots in the eyes."

The writer learned through personal communication that honey is still used for trachoma in the form of eyedrops. A Canadian mother related to him that two of her daughters contracted sore eyes while attending school, where there was an epidemic at the time. They were cured in two or three days by dropping honey into their eyes. It took two and three weeks for the other children in the school to get rid of the same trouble. Cataracts of the eyes were reported to have been cured by the same method, dropping honey into the eyes three times daily.

Our good friend, the famous globe-trotter Dr. W. E. Aughinbaugh, described an operation he witnessed in Panama, during the construction of the canal. A native Indian surgeon of considerable repute performed a disarticulation of the hip joint. He smoked cigarettes incessantly during the operation, laid them down occasionally, picking them up again with his bloody fingers. After the stump was sutured, the surgeon took from a large pail several handfuls of honey, which he smeared over the wound, covering it subsequently with gauze. He assured Dr. Aughinbaugh that he had never had an infection when he applied a layer of honey over the wound. Dr. Aughinbaugh has seen the natives of the Amazon region "suture" extensive injuries by letting beetles unite the margins of wounds with their robust mandibles. After the heads of the insects were severed, the mandibles remained closed and the wounds were covered with honey mixed with liquid wax. The results were excellent.

It is singular that, though honey was used for thousands of years for treatment of wounds and skin troubles, our modern medical literature ignores the subject. Lately, it seems, honey is gradually regaining its age-old repute and lost popularity. Dr. Zaiss, of Heidelberg, considers honey in the treatment of wounds superior to all other ointments. He has treated several thousand cases of severe infections with honey and could not report a single failure. Dr. Zaiss prefers honey even to tincture of iodine. He dresses the wounds with strips of gauze dipped in honey, and finds the wounds perfectly clean in 24 hours. The sloughs, even deep ones, usually adhere to the dressing material. Dr. Zaiss states that the application causes, at first, a transient smarting but the pain is soon relieved and a cooling sensation supervenes. The healing is remarkably rapid. He suggests a daily change of dressing.

The Germans were always firm believers in the curative power of honey, both internally and externally, as a surgical dressing. It is interesting that honey is now combined in Germany with another old popular remedy; namely, cod-liver oil. Pliny highly praised cod-liver oil as a wound dressing (Hist. Nat. 31:27). The Eskimos, Laplanders and the natives of Greenland use cod-liver oil even these days for the dressing of wounds. German surgeons, Zaiss, Sack, Lucke, Buchheister, Löhr, Gundel, Blattner and others, published recently in the medical journals miraculous results which they obtained through the use of a honey-cod-liver oil ointment called Desitin-Honey salve. Infected wounds, ulcerations, burns, fistulas, boils, carbuncles, felons, etc., are reported to heal in the shortest time. The ointment is supposed to check inflammation, stimulate granulation and remove deep necrotic tissues. Subjectively the ointment is very well tolerated because it alleviates pain and eases tension. The change of dressings is not painful because in twenty-four hours the wound is soaked in a rich exudate of lymph which prevents adherence of the dressing material to the wound and is easily removed. The odor of the ointment is rather pleasant, without a corrigent. It is difficult to say whether the honey or the cod-liver oil is the more helpful ingredient but it seems that it is a fortunate combination. The surgeons advise that, though its function is not scientifically proven and therefore justified, these facts should not interfere with its use. In skin diseases, even in psoriasis, the results obtained were excellent. For frostbites on ears, fingers and toes there is nothing which will take out sooner the frost and swelling than when these parts are wrapped in honey. Verrucae (warts) were reported to have been removed by the overnight application of a honey poultice.

Recently Dr. Charles Brunnich, a surgeon of Switzerland, joined the ranks of those who advocate honey for surgical dressings, especially for contused and badly slashed septic wounds. He quotes the case of a man whose finger was smashed in a grinding machine. The bone of the terminal phalanx of the finger was broken and hung on a skin flap. After wrapping the extremity in honey the finger grew on and rapidly healed. Another man had, in succession, two large carbuncles on the back. While the first carbuncle was operated on by a surgeon and left a deep ugly scar, the second was treated only with honey. The cores rapidly eliminated and the wound left only an insignificant scar.

In the *"Alpenländische Bienenzeitung"* (February, 1935) we find the following report from a man: "In the winter of 1933 I heated a boiler of about thirty-five gallons of water. When I opened the cover, it flew with great force against the ceiling. The vapor and hot water poured forth over my unprotected head, over my hands and feet. Some minutes afterward I had violent pains and I believe I would have gone mad if my wife and my daughter had not helped me immediately. They took large pieces of linen, daubed them thickly with honey and put them on my head, neck, hands and feet. Almost instantly the pain ceased. I slept well all night and did not lose a single hair on my head. When the physician came he shook his head and said, 'How can such a thing be possible?' "

PART II

THE HISTORY OF HONEY

CHAPTER XIII

PREHISTORIC TIMES

Preadamitic man, before he changed his habitation and moved from trees to more comfortable quarters in caves and in the process of time became carnivorous, must have delighted in the luscious honey which evidently was plentiful in the forests. The friendship between man and the bees must have been sealed during those good old days, and has been preserved, even deepened, by continuous close contact and mutual service up to the present day. The bees still remain "man's best little friends in the world." They supply him with food, drink, light and medicine.

The human race, since pristine times, has looked upon Nature from the viewpoint of utility. Animals and plants which were most useful or most harmful were always best known to man. It is not surprising, therefore, that bees have been so much in favor since remotest antiquity. Divine Providence would have been devoid of benevolence if she had neglected to produce a creature like the honeybee, so essential to man, "for whom all things were made."

The history of honey is really the history of mankind. Bees, like horses, cattle and sheep, faithfully accompanied man in all his wanderings; they followed him over hills and dales, oceans and rivers, and were the chief witnesses of human civilization. To try to submit a complete history of honey would be a futile effort because there is not even a doubt that it is much older than human records and the race itself. Bees and their products were on our globe long before the Lord proclaimed: "*Faciamus hominem ad imaginem et simili-*

tudinem nostram." (Let us now make man in our image and
likeness.) Genesis Ch. I, v. 26.

We find the earliest traces of bees in the fossil ages. They
were imbedded in amber, preserved by natural inhumation.
Such discoveries have been reported in the Baltic regions of
Germany, in Switzerland and in other parts of Central Europe. The size of these insects was about the same as that of
our honeybees today. Menzel suggested that they looked very
much like the present Italian bees; Tony Kellen, on the other
hand, thought that they seem to represent the Apis adamitica
or pre-adamitica, originating in an era when the human race
did not exist. Pytheas, the Greek navigator and astronomer
(300 B.C.), referred to these fossil bees of the Baltic countries.
Martial, in his epigrams (IV. 32), alludes to bees entombed in
amber, as though buried in honey, immortalized through
their own labors.

> "The bee inclos'd, and through the amber shewn,
>   Seems buried in the juice, which was his own.
>   So honour'd was a life in labor spent:
>   Such might he wish to have his monument."
>   (Translated by Wm. Hay, 1755.)

The petrified bee is an interesting, very rare and unusually
well preserved specimen. It was found only recently in the
browncoal beds of Transylvania. This fossil bee from the
Tertiary strata, imbedded in sandstone hundreds of thousands
of years ago, is also similar to our contemporary honeybee.
The rear legs have the identical rows of brushes, the abdomen consists of six segments separated by lighter colored
bands and the antennae contain the same number of joints.

The oldest evidence that honey was an important human
objective is revealed by a prehistoric painting, discovered in
1919 at Cuevas de la Araña (Spider Cave), northwest of Bi-
corp, Valencia, Spain. This picture, painted in red, is the
most ancient work of art known. It originated in the Stone
Age when man, trying to find shelter from the superabound-
ing beasts, lived in caves. The painting is supposed to be
about 15,000 years old, but as likely as not, it is some
thousand years younger or older. The time-worn fossil relic is
rather primitive but it clearly depicts a man climbing up on
long ropes, probably woven of sedge grass, to a natural hole
in the cliff, which the artist evidently intended to represent

the dwelling of a swarm of wild bees. The man is taking honeycombs out of the cavity and putting them into a bag or basket. Some disturbed bees around the intruder are painted on a scale much larger than that of the human figure (Obermaier). The ancient origin of Spanish cave pictures is confirmed by the fact that many species of animals which are represented in these drawings are extinct today.

Other evidences that honey and wax existed during prehistoric eons are the earthenware colanders found in the lake dwellings of Switzerland, originating in the Neolithic era. That these vessels were employed for straining honey, and possibly also for the utilization of wax, seems more than a conjecture because the inhabitants of the Bernese Alps still use similar vessels for these purposes.

Beyond doubt primitive man obtained honey from wild bees nesting in hollow trees and rocks, a habit which undomesticated bees still pursue. In all probability man cultivated bees as he tamed horses, oxen, sheep and dogs, instituting a cooperative partnership.

CHAPTER XIV

HISTORIC TIMES

We derive our knowledge of the earliest use and importance of honey in historic times from archives of the ancient cultural states, Babylon, Assyria, Persia, India, Egypt,
Greece and Rome. The oldest existing scripts corroborate the
fact that bees were already domesticated creatures and honey
was extensively used for food, drink, medicine and exclusively
for sweetening purposes. Honey was an important commodity.
Taxes and tributes were imposed in the form of payments of
honey and wax. It was equivalent to currency. Today, in the
twentieth century, we could understand the vital importance
of honey in the domestic life of bygone ages only if we were
forced to relinquish completely the use of industrial sugar.
This would overload the imagination of even a most daring
dreamer.

We do not know of any people on earth, including savage
tribes, who did not cultivate bees for their honey with the
exception of the native Indians of the Americas and the
Australian indigenes. Honeybees were unknown to them and
they obtained their scanty supply of honey from stingless
bees.

Before parchment, paper and writing were invented, pictorial engravings on stones conveyed the meaning of human
conceptions. Geometric ideography was the first attempt of
antiquity to express and perpetuate thoughts on lapidary
specimens. Animals and plants were later objects and finally,
anthropomorphic images. We find most petroglyphic carvings
in Egypt, India, Mexico and Peru.

134

EGYPT

The most fertile field, in our historical research, for estab-
lishing the singular and paramount rôle which honey played
in the social, economic and spiritual life of ancient nations is,
unquestionably, Egypt, the land of Pharaohs. The oldest hieroglyphic carvings in temples, on sarcophagi and obelisks sufficiently prove that bees and honey had a vital significance in
the daily life of the population of Egypt. These monuments
symbolically perpetuate bees and their principal product,
honey. On the Flamic and Pamphilic obelisks (Amada), on
the famous Rosetta stone, on the pillars of the Temple of
Karnak and on the obelisk of Luxor (which was erected in
1836 on the Place de la Concorde, Paris), we find many
images of bees. On the colossal sarcophagus of Rameses III
(20th Dynasty) in the Musée Louvre, on the sarcophagus of a
priest who died during the reign of Psametic I (26th Dynasty) and on a granite statue of Rameses II, there are
numerous such designs. King Menes, the founder of the First
Dynasty of Egyptian Kings, the date of whose role is var-
iously given as 4000 to 5000 B.C. (according to Brugsch, 4445
B.C.), was called "the Beekeeper." Tony Kellen found some
writing on one of the Louvre papyri which suggested that it
had been a restaurant check and honey was among the food
consumed.

Next to hieroglyphic representations, the wall paintings of
the royal tombs demonstrate the great national importance of
honey. There are only a few funeral vaults in which bees and
honey are not represented pictorially. Honeycombs, honey
cakes, sealed jars of honey and lotus blooms were placed next
to the sarcophagi as food for the souls of the dead. In the
tomb of Pa-Ba-Sa, in Thebes, the entire wall is decorated by
rows of bees. A man is shown pouring honey into a pail,
another is kneeling and praying before a pyramid of honeycombs. On the wall of the tomb of Rekh-Mi-Re all phases of
the honey industry are depicted; how the combs were removed from the hives with the aid of smoke, the baking of
honey cakes, the filling and sealing of jars, etc.

From a literary aspect there is little left in Egypt so far as
the subject is concerned. During the conflagration of 312
B.C., the great library of Alexandria was totally destroyed and
all its treasures and documents were lost. It is remarkable
that one of their seers predicted this catastrophe when he

said: "Oh Egypt . . . only unbelievable legends will remain for later generations . . . engraved on stones, monuments, obelisks and pyramids."

The Egyptian Papyri, representing the oldest civilization of the world, often refer to honey, especially to its medicinal value. Almost all Egyptian medicines contained honey, wine and milk. Honey sacrifices were offered to the deities. The frequent symbolical use of bees in Egypt must be attributed not only to the fact that honey was an important article of commerce and a valuable food and medicinal substance but to the admiration of the Egyptians for the diligence, industry, order, economy, endurance, intelligence and courage of the bees and their loyalty to a sovereign. The bees are the only creatures which are entirely subjugated to a ruler. Next to the signatures of Egyptian kings there was a figure of a bee. Apiculture was far advanced in Egypt, likewise in Babylonia and in Assyria.

The ancient Egyptians were habitual beer drinkers. The land was ill-suited to the cultivation of the grape-vine. Xenophon (400 B.C.) mentions an Egyptian beverage made of wheat, barley and honey. On the decline of the Egyptians and the rise of the Greeks and Romans, wine made of grapes became a drink of civilization.

INDIA

Soulful India was supposed to be not only the cradle of humanity but also the birthplace of the bee. The latter claim was, however, contested by both Egypt and Greece. In ancient Indian scripts we find scanty information about apiculture. They allude to honey and bees more from mythological, poetical, philosophical, moral and religious viewpoints. The Rig-Veda, written about 3000 B.C., often mentions honey. To the population of India honey represented everything that was sweet and beneficial. The Hindu had to turn his right side toward the beehive, as though passing a deity. God Krishna was symbolized by a bee and was called *madhava*, born in honey. The Hindu believed that whoever ate honey would become strong, rich, happy and wise and that it would improve not only his own looks but would influence even his offspring.

In India, due to the fertility of the soil and the abundance of water and sunlight, the animals and plants are the largest on earth. The bees are no exception. *Apis dorsata,* the giant bee of India, builds enormous combs, often six feet square, suspended from the highest trees, hanging rocks and other inaccessible places to gain protection from man and beast. The combs are visible from a distance of miles. Special honey hunters approach the nests with ladders and ropes, usually at night time, to collect their plentiful harvest.*

Honey had a popular use in India as a food and medicine and in the preparation of alcoholic drinks. The Hindus drank *madhuparka,* a mixture of honey and curds, during religious ceremonies with the toast: "I drink thee for luck, glory, power, and for the enjoyment of food."

CHINA

In China, the home of sugar-cane, honey was used less than in any other country. There was no need of honey as a sweetening substance because cane-juice was plentiful. The Chinese did not cultivate bees for this reason. Besides, the bees caused considerable damage to sugar plantations and also plundered the syrup during the process of extraction. Honey was used by the Chinese more as a medicinal substance and a complement to diets. In the interior of China, even today, honey can be obtained only in old-style medicine shops. *Mi-tsao* or honey-jujube is a popular confection in China. It is made from honey and *jujuba* (Zizyphus vulgaris), a red fruit shaped like a date. The Chinese often mix their opium with honey.

GREECE

The solemn and prominent part honey played in the history of Greece is conclusively proven by its mythology. Ambrosia, the food, and nectar, the drink of the gods, were made of honey. The *Iliad* (XI. 630) refers to honey as the food of kings. The honey of Mt. Hymettus was a daily food of Athens. This mountain was covered with odoriferous wild flowers, principally thyme, and the air was scented with the fragrance of the blooms. The bees were partial to these hills.

---

* *Apis indica,* the "hive-bee" of India and of China, is not only smaller in size than our honeybee but is somewhat different in behavior.

(It is singular that the population of ancient Greece, a maritime country *par excellence*, as fond as they were of honey, utterly neglected sea-food. Homer in the *Iliad* never mentions fish; in the *Odyssey*, Menelaus complains that he and his men were so hungry that they were compelled to eat fish.)

Ancient Attica, with its area of forty square miles, recorded twenty thousand hives during the time of Pericles (429 B.C.). All ancient Greek authors praised the medicinal and nutrimental value of Attic honey, "the crowning dish of all feasts." The oldest ruins in the rural districts of Greece are buildings which originally housed the hives. These stone edifices were built high, to outwit the cunning of the bears, arch enemies of bees and bosom friends of honey.

THE ROMAN EMPIRE

In the ancient Roman Empire honey was in great abundance. All Mediterranean states surrounding this glorious sea were veritable honey-lands. During the second Punic War (218–201 B.C.), apiculture was already flourishing. Honey production was practiced at a much earlier date in Greece and the art was conveyed by the Phoenicians and early Greek settlers to the Italian peninsula.

Virgil, the poet laureate of bees, was the greatest glorifier of honey. Book IV of *Georgics* is a panegyric on "heaven-born" honey. *Protinus œrii mellis caelestia dona exsequar*, is the first line of Georgics (next I sing of honey, the heavenly ethereal gift). Virgil often bepraises even in the *Aeneid* the "sweet-scented honey, fragrant with thyme."

Pliny in the XIth book of his *Historia Naturalis* devotes many chapters to honey, "which the bees collect from the sweet juices of flowers, so beneficial to health." From Pliny's very voluminous works (thirty-seven books) we derive much information. This most prolific writer, who quotes no less than twenty-five hundred authors, had great admiration for honey and assembled all the Egyptian, Greek and Latin knowledge on the subject. Pliny also describes the contemporary honey industry in Italy, in old Germania and in the British Isles during the Roman invasion. Pliny refers to eight-feet long "honey-slabs," brought from Alemannia. All other Latin writers speak in high terms of bees and honey. Cicero remarks in *De Senectute* that he considers the successful production of honey essential to good farming and describes how the slaves collected wild honey in the forests. Foods and drinks, mixed with honey, were seldom missing on the daily menus of ancient Rome.* It was a courteous act of the Romans to offer a respected guest some honey, fresh from the hives. The host welcomed his visitors with the words: "Here is honey which God provided for your health." Snails destined for the royal tables were fattened and sweetened with honey.

ANCIENT BRITAIN

Pliny quoted the reports of ancient voyagers, who found in the present BRITISH ISLES a honey-brew which was freely consumed by the Islanders. This was long before the Roman conquest of the Islands, so the assumption that bee culture was introduced into England by the Romans is erroneous. Undoubtedly, apiculture was of vital importance in the Roman Empire, because its triumphant armies, when invading foreign territories, carried their beehives with them. The Britons must have broadened their knowledge of bee-craft during the Roman invasion.

That beekeeping was an outstanding pursuit among the Britons is illustrated by Tickner Edwardes' graphic account in his delightful book, *The Lore of the Honey-Bee.* "Among the Anglo-Saxons the beehives supplied the whole nation, from the king down to the poorest serf, not only with an important part of their food but with drink and light as well. . . . Britain was known among the early Druid bards as the Isle of Honey." (The Honey Isle of Beli was another bardic name for Britain.)

"British History begins"—Edwardes continues—"with the record of the first voyage of the Phoenicians, who adventuring farther than any other of their intrepid race, chanced upon the Scilly Isles and the neighbouring coast of Cornwall and thence brought back their first cargo of tin. The whereabouts of the Phoenician 'Barat-Anac,' The Country of Tin, remained a secret probably for ages, jealously guarded by these ancient mariners, the first true seamen that the world had ever known. They were expert navigators, venturing

---

* *Mulsum,* four-fifths wine and one-fifth honey, was a favorite drink of the Romans. *Hydromel,* which is really mead, was used as a medicine.

enormous distances overseas, even in King Solomon's time, and that was a thousand years before the advent of Caesar. In all likelihood, they had been in frequent communication with the Britons, centuries before the Greeks took to searching for this wonderful tin-bearing land, and still longer before the name Barat-Anac became corrupted into the Britannia of the Romans. And it is hardly to be supposed that a people of so ancient a civilization, and of so great a repute in the sciences and refinements of life, as the Phoenicians—a people from whom the early Greeks themselves had learned the art and practice of letters—could remain in touch, century after century, with a nation like the Britons without effecting in them enormous improvement and development in every way that would appeal to so high-mettled and competent a race."

Honey must have been abundant in the British Isles, another veritable land of milk and honey. The Welsh and Celtic legends teem with references to sparkling mead and honey drinks. The chief Irish God, Manannan, praised the island-paradise (Isle of Man), where:

> Rivers pour forth a stream of honey
> In the land of Manannan, son of Lêr
> ....
> Abundant there are honey and wine,
> Death and decay thou wilt not see.

Tributes were paid with mead and honey and the laws fixed the amount which had to be delivered to the chieftains. The measures which the laws mention (Brehon Law Tracts) prove that honey must have been plentiful: A *milch-cow* measure of honey could be lifted by an average individual up to his knees; a *large heifer* measure of honey one could raise to the waist; a *small heifer*, to the shoulder; and a *dairt*, over one's head. The shell of an egg was also used to measure smaller quantities of honey; twelve of these equaled about a pint.

There is frequent mention that the ancient Britons used honey for cooking and baking. Meat and fish were often cooked in honey, and they mixed their porridge with it. The principal use of honey was, however, in the preparation of alcoholic drinks.

From most ancient times *merrie England* was drenched in ale. Unquestionably it was their national drink. The ale-wife, depicted with two cups in her hands, so gloriously immortal-

ized, was the symbol of old English inns. Ale was considered
a wholesome liquor which supported the natural heat and
moisture of the body and "there is no drink which conduceth
more to the preservation of one and the increase of the other
than Ale." While the English drank ale they were strong,
brawny and able men and "could draw an arrow an ell long
but when they fell to wine and beer, they were found to be
impaired in strength and age."

The old Saxon ale or mead was not a malt liquor but
"made from honey or the washing of the honeycombs." The
name ale came into the English language during the Danish
invasion of England and was derived from the Danish word
"öl." The mead or meth of the Norse and Teutonic forefa-
thers was made of honey. The big and burly gods with prodi-
gious droughtiness and appetite indulged in a copious supply
of strong mead which never failed. The Valkyries, the tall
and beautiful maidens, were the modern barmaids.

Mead held its sway in old England at least for a thousand
years. The Anglo-Saxon forebears indulged generously in
mead, a habit they seem to have inherited from the Teutonic
heroes. These chieftains were accu__d of gluttony and drunk-
enness and of going to battle drunk with mead, "bringing
about the ruin of Britain."

"Hop-drinks" were introduced into England by the Flem-
ish immigrants. Hop was considered for a long time as an
adulterant and the "wicked weed" was checked by legislation, even prohibited because it not only "spoilt the taste of
the drink but endangered the lives of the people." A century
of industrial progress in manufacturing beer undoubtedly improved its quality. Wine always was, and still is considered
the "beverage of the rich." The whiskey of the Irish and the
Scotch invaded England only at a very late date.

The Saxon "beor" meant mead (beo=bee) and the term
"beer" was undoubtedly derived from it. On many old English inns we find the sign of a beehive often accompanied by
some rhyme. At Grantham, which boasts of a three hundred
foot high steeple, there is a real beehive set up before the inn
with the following inscription:

"Stop! Traveller, this wondrous sign explore,
And say when thou hast viewed it o'er,
Grantham, now, two rarities are thine,
A lofty steeple and a living sign."

Before a Birmingham inn there is the verse:

"In this hive we all are alive,
    Good liquor makes us funny!
If you be dry, step in and try
    The value of our honey."

GERMANY

In Germany, honey production has always been an outstanding and favorite occupation. Few nations have studied the economy and management of bees more thoroughly than the Germans. Possibly this has contributed to their far-famed thrift.

Forest apiculture preceded everywhere the cultivation of bees by cottagers and farmers. German apiculture must have been far advanced before the invasion of the Romans, the emissaries of continental culture. Pytheas and Massilia (after whom Marseilles was named), contemporaries of Alexander the Great, described that on a journey of exploration they found meth (honey-wine, often mentioned in the Niebelungen Saga) excessively used in old Alemannia, and that the inhabitants covered their bread with honey. The record in itself proves that honey must have been in great abundance. And this was four hundred years before the Christian era. Pliny's reference to the enormous honeycombs of Germania would indicate that they were removed from hollow tree-trunks. There are many traces among the ancient laws of Germany that litigations concerning honey production and especially swarming were quite frequent. Special tribunals adjudged these disputes.

Charlemagne in his famous "Capitulares Karlomanni" gave strict orders pertaining to honey industry. Chapter V described honey, mead and wax in minutest details. Chapter XX directed the population to take an inventory every year of their honey and mead supply. Upon the introduction of Christianity, honey production increased greatly in Germany on account of the demand for wax for church candles. Monasteries were invariably cultivators of bees. Mead must also have been plentiful, judging from an ancient record that a fire in Meissen, on the Upper-Elba, in 1015, was extinguished with mead because the inhabitants were short of water.

Land-rule (dominium) was universal in Germany and the

phrase *in signum vel recognitionem dominii* (in mark and acknowledgment of land-rule) was a traditional expression. The lands were mainly owned by princes and the Church. Those who lived in such lands were obliged to pay taxes in honey and wax. Honey and wax were considered royal or princely gifts and religious people freely contributed them to the Church.

The German honey industry was closely associated with the Lüneburger Heide. These plains of stormy historical background have been a real paradise of bees and the favorite topic of German poets. The province of Hanover in which these plains are located is famous for its honey. The level land, covered with primitive vegetation, mainly heather, is unusually rich in nectar. This section of the country has been preserved in a wild state by the bees and its primitive beauty is under their protection. Few men and beasts ever approach the localities, fearing the proverbial anger of these insects. Usually a narrow path leads to the beestands; a beaten track made by the bee-fathers for the collection of honey.

The honey market of Breslau, on Maundy Thursday, was famous for centuries, and the day is celebrated even now with festivities. There were many mead breweries in Münich, Ulm on the Danube, Danzig, Riga, etc. According to old documents, "the judge sat in court with a jug of mead before him, so filled to the brim that a fly could drink from its border."

Honey production suffered a noticeable decline at the end of the sixteenth and beginning of the seventeenth centuries due to the Thirty Years' War. It was neglected for many years before and after this long conflict. Germany also suffered a similar setback during the World War. It is noteworthy that in the course of the same period, beekeeping made a great advance in the United States and Great Britain.

FRANCE

With the possible exception of the Germans and the Slavic races, there are only a few nations on the European continent who held honey in higher esteem than the French. The French regarded it as a life-giving substance much the same as bread and milk. Their folklore, fables, laws and religious customs give evidence of the importance of honey in the daily life of the nation.

Historical records substantiate the fact that beekeeping was a foremost industry in France. The ancient Barons derived considerable revenue from taxes imposed upon beehives. The lords of the land were permitted to collect tax from the people who hunted for honey in their forests and, at a later period, from those who cultivated bees there. A certain proportion of honey and wax had to be relinquished by the vassals. The French Government also imposed taxes on beehives. In 1791, when the government demanded from the prefects of the provinces an exact record of hives, the population, fearing an additional tax, destroyed their hives in preference to paying higher taxes. After that, for a long time, apiculture was wholly neglected in France.

The taxation of beekeeping in France was not solely a medieval custom. A fairly recent fiscal legislation (1934) imposes a tax on beehives. According to this new law, if a beekeeper feeds his bees on his own property he is assessed with a tax on agricultural products; but if his bees feed on the grounds of his neighbors the tax is higher because the revenue classes as non-commercial business. (The revenue collectors must have a difficult time keeping their eyes on the bees, to ascertain whether they remain at home or pay business or social calls.)

*   *   *

The *Island of Corsica*, comprising 3790 square miles, had to pay 200,000 pounds of wax as a yearly tribute to the Romans, which means that they produced at least three million pounds of honey. *Holland*, especially Friesland, had several thousand hives to the square mile. *Spain* teemed with beehives. Ex-King Alfonso was an ardent bee lover and was keenly interested in apiculture. In the park of the royal palace he had about a thousand colonies of bees and many more hives on his country estates. The leading apiculturist of Spain, Antonio Garay Victoria, had 1500 colonies on his estate in Claveria.

HUNGARY

The ancient Roman province of Pannonia, which consisted of Hungary, Austria, Slavonia, Styria, Croatia, Bosnia, etc., was another veritable honey-land. The prevalence of bees along the Danube is verified by the statement of Herodotus

(484 B.C.) who remarked that at certain intersections it was impossible to cross the river on account of bees. The Turks used beehives to thwart hostile crossings of the Danube.

Hungary always was and still is an Eldorado of bees. Priscus, who in 448 A.D. traversed Hungary with the Greek emissaries sent to King Attila, reported that he was liberally provided there with mead. Historical records show that the population of Hungary had to supply the monasteries with honey and wax. The blind king, Bela II (1138 A.D.), donated sixty beekeepers to an Abbey to attend the hives. One Palatinate produced as much as ten thousand barrels of mead. The redolent acacia honey of Hungary has always been considered one of the finest in the world.

AUSTRIA

In Austria, both Upper and Lower, likewise in Salzburg, Tyrol, Voralberg, Styria, Carinthia, Carniola and in the other former provinces of Istria, Dalmatia, Galicia and Bukowina, beekeeping was an important industry. There were many apicultural schools and societies with frequent meetings and festivals. All members of the Imperial house of Hapsburg, since the reign of the great Empress Maria Theresa, who founded the Apicultural College in Vienna (1769), were enthusiastic supporters of apiculture and lovers of honey.

THE SLAVIC COUNTRIES

All Slavic races were partial to honey production. They used honey freely on their bread, mixed it with curds and butter, employed it in baking and in the preparation of alcoholic drinks. The Russians and Poles were experts in making hot honey drinks, and there are many popular winter beverages on the European continent which originated in Russia. The Poles were reputed to be the brewers of finest mead.

The Slavs were widely disseminated over Eastern, Southeastern and Central Europe and Asia. The Russians, Poles, Ruthenians, Serbs, Croatians, Lithuanians, Czechs, Moravians, Slovaks, Wends, Bosnians, Montenegrins and Slovens were all ardent bee-lovers. The old Prussians and Silesians belonged originally to Slavic races but were later absorbed by the ancient Teutons who inherited the Slavic fondness for honey. The Slavic interbreeding with the Hungarians, the Bulgarians, the Northern Finnish and Tartar races spread this lickerish tendency among the respective lands.

Poland was especially rich in honey. Gallus, who explored Poland in the eleventh century, remarked *pane et carne et melle satis est copiosa* (there is plenty of bread, meat and honey) and stated further *ubi aer salubris, ager fertilis, silva melliflua* (where the air is salubrious, the fields are fertile and the forests flow with honey). One of their beekeepers, Piast, who treated the royal electors with mead which never diminished, was elected king and his descendants ruled over Poland for several centuries. In the fourteenth century, Poland sold honey in foreign markets which yielded millions of florins in export duties to the royal treasury.

Of Poland we read many fantastic tales, in themselves an indication of the enormous honeycombs which filled hollow trees in the forests. William Harrison, in *Holinshed's Chronicles* (1577), mentions (III, Ch. 4) that in Poland the honeycombs were so great and abundant that huge bears fell into them and were drowned before they could recover and find a means of escape.

THE AMERICAN CONTINENT

As already mentioned, there were only two continents on our globe where the honeybee was non-existent, the Americas and Australia. When John Eliot translated the Bible into the language of the North American aborigines he could not even find expressive terms in their phraseology for honey and wax.

Previous to the importation of the German bees (brown or black), there were, however, other honey-collecting bees in the Americas, such as the stingless bees (Trigonae and Meliponae), the size of domestic flies, which occasionally bite like ants and then rub their poison of rancid odor into the wound. Columbus found their honey and wax in abandoned huts. The South Americans call them "Angelitos," little angels, because they do not sting. They nest, as a rule, in the hollows of dead trees, but occasionally make their own hives in the ground or attached to the branches of trees. There are evidences that the Indians cultivated them and supplied them with wooden logs and earthenware jars in which to nest.

The honey which these stingless bees produce is rather

thin but of an agreeable aromatic odor; the natives even prefer it to the honey of the white man's "stinging fly" and attribute greater remedial value to it. The combs are not as regular as those of the honeybee; they form an irregular mass of cells but are occasionally hexagon shaped.

That honey had an important part in the lives of the natives before the discovery of America is proven by the ancient Mayan and Aztec codices. The conquered tribes had to pay tributes of honey. The Codex Mendoza lists the tributes of seven hundred pottery jars of honey paid to Montezuma, the Aztec emperor of Mexico. Some of the sacred books mention that the conquering heroes permitted the defeated tribes to pursue pottery making and beekeeping, apparently two of their most important occupations. Many hieroglyphic carvings represent bees and honeycombs, and human figures carrying on their backs large jars, containing honey, as a tribute.

Honey was unquestionably used as a food and for the preparation of intoxicating beverages. The Mexican mead (acan) was probably not unlike the mead of other nations. It is mentioned that it was health-giving and intoxicating, similar to the drinks made of pulque. The Mexican Indians had their bee-gods to whom they prayed for plenty of honey. There are several folk tales of the South American Indians connected with hunting for wild honey which are remarkably similar to those of the Russians, the Hindus, the African and East Indian natives. (See page 161.)

Honeybees (Apis Mellifica) were brought to the American Continent by the Spanish, Dutch and English settlers at the end of the seventeenth century. In Mexico they were domesticated much earlier than in the United States. We find the first traces of bees in the United States in Boston in 1644, where they were imported by the English. A hurricane carried them over the Alleghany Mountains. Their tendency to migrate southward was very expressed. The bees found a new home in the United States in much the same manner as did the European settlers.

Toward the second half of the eighteenth century (1764) the bees were taken from Spanish Florida to Cuba, where, however, they did not remain very long. The planters soon annihilated them because they robbed the sugar-canes. The bees rapidly multiplied in Cuba. M. Montelle (*Choix de Lectures Geographiques et Historiques, Tome 5, Part II*)

says, in speaking of the island of Cuba: "When the Floridas
were ceded in 1763 by Spain to England, the five or six
hundred miserable beings who vegetated in those regions,
took refuge in Cuba, and carried with them some Bees: these
useful insects repaired to the forests, established themselves
in the hollows of old trees, and multiplied with a celerity
which appeared incredible. The hives yield four crops every
year and the swarms succeed each other without interrup-
tion." Don Ulloa in *Philosophical and Historical Memoirs,*
concerning the discovery by Spain, also refers to bees:
"These insects multiplied to such a degree, that they spread to
the mountains and were prejudicial to the sugar-canes, on
which they fed. Their fecundity was so great that a hive
yielded a swarm and sometimes two in a month. The wax is
uncommonly white and the honey of perfect transparency
and of exquisite taste." In the Barbadoes, the bees did not
visit flowers but lived in the midst of sugar refineries. In
Argentina, Australia, and New Zealand the bees made their
appearance around 1840, in Brazil in 1848, and in Chile and
Peru only in 1857.

IN THE UNITED STATES

In the United States, the honeybees spread very rapidly.
The American Indians looked upon them as the harbingers of
misfortune. It seems as though they were right, and the
prophecy was well-grounded. Longfellow referred to it in
"Hiawatha":

"Wheresoe'er they move, before them
Swarms the stinging fly, the Ahmo,
Swarms the Bee, the honey-maker;
Wheresoe'er they tread, beneath them
Springs a flower unknown among us,
Springs the White Man's Foot in blossom."*

The Indians called the bees the "white man's flies" or "English flies." They were the heralds of American civilization,
and when the Indians perceived a swarm in the forest they
shouted: "The pale-faced intruders are coming, they will soon
be here!" The bees swiftly covered the West. Washington

---

* White clover.

Irving remarked that in the proportion that the bees advanced, the Indians and the buffaloes retired. (*Tour in the Prairies.*)

The bees spread in swarms from the Atlantic Coast toward the Pacific. The old settlers recorded the time when bees first crossed the Mississippi. The West was a real paradise for these nectar-seeking insects, another veritable land of promise. William Cullen Bryant vividly described the seething activity of the bee in the new country, where she—

> "Fills the Savannahs with her murmurings,
> And hides her sweets, as in the golden age,
> Within the hollow oak. I listen long
> To her domestic hum, and think I hear
> The sound of that advancing multitude,
> Which soon shall fill the deserts."

The first honeybees were taken to California in March, 1853. They flourished in the Santa Clara valley, sending off as many as three swarms during the first season. How highly valued they were is best proven by the fact that during the settlement of the estate of a land owner, named Shelton, who had been killed, two colonies of bees were sold at auction for $105 and $110, respectively. It is recorded that four swarms were imported to California from the East Coast in 1859. The hives were placed in the rear of covered wagons. The pioneers occasionally stopped to allow the bees to hover about the flower-pastures within their reach, until darkness, when the hives were again closed.

The West, especially California, as described by Muir, was one sweet bee garden, from the snowy Sierras to the ocean, where the "bee-flowers" bloomed in lavish abundance. Plows and sheep made a sad havoc of these glorious pastures, destroying like wildfire tens of thousands of flowery acres, and banishing many species of the best honey plants, for which loss cultivation so far has given no adequate compensation. The rich primeval soil of the United States was covered with thick forests, profuse vegetation and wild flowers. The settlers, however, lumbered the forests, slaughtered wild animals, tilled the soil, destroyed the surface moisture and created droughts by offsetting the equilibrium of Nature's forces. They worked the land for all it was worth and planted, instead of soil-building, soil-depleting crops. The recent formation of the Western, so-called dust-bowl, seems to be a "vendetta" of the bees.

The bees preferred the woods to comfortable hives. Forests provided them with shelter, food and good protection against the elements, the cold of winter and the heat of summer; against rains and storms and, besides, kept their treasures concealed. They made a nest in any suitable place. Muir told how a friend of his, hunting in the San Joaquin valley, sat down on a coon-trap to rest, but soon was surrounded by an angry crowd of bees. He discovered that he had been sitting upon their hive which contained over two hundred pounds of honey.

Contemporary newspapers related how bees also made their nests in abandoned houses. When the old Hawes homestead in Yarmouth, Mass., which had sheltered many generations of Cape Cod people, was doomed to be torn down, the workmen could not approach the ruins because the bees resented their intrusion and the demolishing had to be postponed until cold weather set in. The walls of the building were found to be solidly packed with honeycombs and hundreds of pounds of honey were removed.

Bees have always suffered from drought. During the famine of the dry year 1877, it is said that the fate of the bees was the saddest of all. In Los Angeles and San Diego counties, one-half to three-fourths of the bees perished from sheer starvation. Not less than eighteen thousand colonies were lost in these two counties alone, and in others the loss was equally as great. The latest disastrous droughts and floods in the United States played havoc among the bees.

Next to successive droughts and floods there is a new danger brought on by civilization, which lurks behind apiculture, namely, the indiscriminate use of poisonous dust and liquid sprays which commercial airplanes broadcast to protect the orchards and other plantations from injurious insects. This practice is daily increasing in the West and in some Eastern States. In one county of California alone there were seventeen pilots licensed in 1936 to engage in pest control.

The arsenical sprays drift to large areas, partly spread by the propellers of the airplanes, partly by the velocity of air currents. The destructive poisons often drift three to five miles from the places over which they are applied. This is dangerous not only to the bees but also to livestock and to public health. If the poison does not kill older bees, the tainted pollen which they carry into the hives will destroy the brood. This high-pressure application of sprays and dusters (3000 to 5000 pounds at a time) is a dangerous practice. The benefits which are derived from this procedure may be outweighed by the loss of the pollinating services of bees, besides a great decrease in honey production. It is noteworthy that so far not a single instance has been found of any of the arsenic getting into the honey.

Among the Southern States, Texas was another "land flowing with milk and honey." To quote J. Taylor Allen (*Early Pioneer Days of Texas*), "Honey Grove (Texas) derived its name from the immense number of bee trees of richest honey; deposited in every hollow tree, and sometimes in the tangled down weeds and grass. David Crockett and my father W. B. Allen and his pioneer comrades found here honey in abundance in the early days of Texas. Oh, what happy, indescribable times we would have if we could find such country again, but gone forever. . . . Honey Grove— let the name perpetuate the meaning that its name implies; a grove where industry, economy, enterprise and perseverance shall be perpetuated. It is said that Davy Crockett and his men, those illustrious Texan heroes, camped here a week on their way to that world-famed Alamo, and fed on the honey that gave them the joy of Service and Zeal for their country's cause. . . . I cannot refrain from paying tribute to the industrious bees. How diligently they gather and economically store during the season of labor that they may have plenty in the storehouses in the winter. What a lesson to us the bees give, teaching us the need for industry, thrift and economy, using our God-given talent while it is day and laying in store for the day when our work is done. . . . Nor shall I forget the nectar of the gods, the honey furnished us by the industrious honey bee, the most wonderful insect in God's creation, flitting from flower to flower, extracting here a little and there a little and gathering the sweetest of all sweets. If there is anything I like better than honey it is . . . more honey."

During the Civil War, soldiers carried off beehives.

AMERICAN HONEY-LORE

In American folklore, young as it is, we find many tales which reflect on honey. H. B. Parks, in "The Lost Honey Mines in Texas," *Southwest Review*, (1930. 16.) remarks: "The best place and time to hear honey-cave stories is some bee-yard in the chaparral of Southwest Texas, when the extracting crew is resting around the campfire after a hard day's work. From the prevalence and absurdity of the legends, however, it is safe to infer that they are of long standing."

"The tales of bee-caves have much in common with stories about lost mines," Parks continues. . . . The mouths of the caves were supposed to be guarded by huge rattlesnakes, vicious bats, scorpions; occasionally, by ghosts. Usually, as the story goes, some surveyor entered the cave about thirty years ago and reported vast rooms filled with honey in pure white combs. Often a well-driller in the vicinity has passed, they say, through just thirty feet of honey and wax. And someone can always (for a certain consideration and not otherwise) show you the location of the cave.

The Story of Bee Mountain, as described by Parks, is very popular. It was disclosed to two boys by a cowpuncher who was well acquainted with the mountain and who had procured plenty of honey there himself. According to the informant, this mountain was a hollow hill, conical in shape and several thousand feet in height. On one side was an opening; and if the searchers could have used sulphur fumes, sufficiently strong to stupefy the bees, they might have entered the interior of the mountain, where hundreds and thousands of pounds of honey were suspended from the roof. There was also a rumor afloat that some boys had attempted to invade it, but they were frightened away by Cherokee Indians.

Another story, according to Parks, was told by a man who could remember that during his early childhood Indians would come after every wet spring to obtain honey from bees living in colonies, attached to the undersurface of a wide projecting rock at the top of a nearby cliff, some seventy feet above the bed of a river. The Indians reached the honey by splicing together mesquite poles. Then some light Indian would climb the pole and the others would move it from place to place, while the Indian aloft lowered the honeycombs by means of a rope and a grass sack. Once a group of hostile Indians came to gather some honey, and after they had obtained all they desired, turned on the white settlers and killed many of them. Mr. Parks visited Bee Mountain several years ago, and counted some three hundred colonies of bees attached to an overhanging rock. At the base of the bluff were the remains of hundreds of pieces of mesquite poles, formerly parts of ladders used probably by the Indians.

"Bee Cave up Blanco" seems to be famous everywhere except along the Blanco River. An old hunter said that one man in his party had climbed to the mouth of a great cave along the banks of the river. On arriving at the opening, he was completely covered by thousands of bees and he was saved from being stung to death only by his heavy clothing. He was able to drive the bees from his eyes just long enough to obtain a glimpse of the cave, where he beheld a solid wall of white honeycombs. The man later returned with a companion, and with the aid of smoke and the light of torches the hunters were enabled to enter this gigantic hive. They were approaching beautiful sheets of honeycombs when a warning note caused them to look to the floor of the cave. Horrified, they discovered that they were standing at the edge of what appeared to be a solid mass of wriggling, twisting rattlesnakes. The hunters, by quick movement, regained the entrance in safety.

Another famous bee cave, Parks continues, is reported to be located very close to the City of San Marcos, in the side of a cliff. The entire rock composing the bluff is full of holes and this is the home, not only of an immense colony of bees, but also of many snakes, rattlesnakes being predominant. According to the story, a group of men tried to open a hole in the side of this bluff. The leader said that he had been assured that there were hundreds of pounds of honey and beeswax in the cave, and he felt certain that this treasure could be obtained with the aid of a patented smoke gun which he possessed. Carrying the famous smoke gun and a lantern, one of the members explored the cave to a depth of several thousands of feet. He returned with the report that enormous amounts of honey and wax were almost at their finger tips. The exploring company tried to enlarge the opening, but as soon as they commenced to pound on the rock, snakes began to issue from every little hole in the face of the bluff, and, while no one was hurt, the sight was so terrible that the men fled and no amount of hidden treasure could induce them to return.

The bee cave in the Davis Mountains is another place that can be "easily" approached. The opening is as large as the doorway of an immense cathedral. With proper protection a person can enter the cave and is at once astonished by the curtainlike sheets of honeycomb which hang from the ceiling. As far as one penetrates into the cave this white honey-

comb extends, one sheet right after another. The terrible
thing about the cave, however, is supernatural. The first
thing that attracts the attention of the explorer is the fact
that he is standing in the midst of dozens of human skeletons.
If he proceeds, he feels a sudden chill in the atmosphere and
something seems to take hold of him in such a way that he
cannot move farther inward, although he can see nothing to
stop him. If the adventurer does not heed the warning and
tries to go still farther, he is crushed by an unknown force
and falls dead to the floor. Should his companions attempt to
remove the body, they, too, are stricken with death and add
to this pile of grim reminders of the force which protects the
honey bees of the Davis Mountains. (All these stories are
somewhat reminiscent of the legend about the four Greeks,
who tried to plunder the grotto of Zeus.)

The cave up the Nueces is thought to be located in the
face of a cliff some thousand feet in height. During the
spring season, to one standing on the top of the bluff, the
bees going and coming from the mouth of the cave resemble
a great stream of smoke; and the hum of their wings is so
loud that the roar can be heard for miles. According to the
story, thirty years ago a surveyor discovered a second entrance and, making a torch of his coat, went into the cave,
protected by the smoke of the burning garment. He passed
through room after room filled with long white sheets of
purest guajillo honey, and estimated that the cave contained
several million pounds. Some of the combs were at least fifty
feet from top to bottom. Before the surveyor had time to
make the proper preparations to remove the honey, he fell
sick and died. Just before his death, he called a doctor and
gave him a map showing the entrance to the bee cave. A
story was current in San Antonio some five or six years ago
that this map was on sale for $500. A second version is that a
ranchman living near this canyon had a well drained for
water. Some fifty feet down, the drill-bit entered a cavity,
and when a sand bucket was substituted for the rock-bit,
honey and beeswax were brought up in great quantities. The
cavity was thirty feet from top to bottom.

Another story, Parks relates, is that of an old beekeeper
and former cowboy, "Jones," who said that up the Nueces
canyon the whole wall was filled with bees. With a companion, he planned to take advantage of the bees, and to become
rich by selling honey. "Jones" and his friend bought a black-

smith's bellows and made a machine, which they mounted on a sled, for blowing sulphur fumes. A honey extractor was placed on another sled. The men then bought two colonies of bees and several burros. When the cave-bees had finished gathering the spring crop of honey, "Jones" and a curious caravan set out for the canyon. At the mouth of the canyon, the party made camp. The next day they pushed the smoke engine as far as the first bee cave, fired it up, and pumped the fumes into the skeleton rock that guarded the honey. After a hard day's work, the bees in this cave were all killed. That night, two colonies of bees in hives were placed in front of the cave. The next day these hive-bees worked overtime, stealing the honey from the cave. In the evening, "Jones" and his companion, as the story goes, extracted three hundred pounds of honey which they had secured with the aid of these two colonies. Elated by the success of the scheme, they sent for more colonies. By the use of the smoke-machine and by moving from cave to cave, the men were soon keeping a regular line of burros busy carrying honey to the city and returning with empty cans. The bees worked so hard that the colonies had to be replaced every two weeks. Unfortunately winter put an end to this performance.

Honey caves have been the object of many expeditions, Parks concludes. Such quests for hidden sweets were often broached by country-boys, generally without definite plan or reliable information, except that someone had told of a bee cave somewhere, and they were determined to get the honey. The stories that have appeared in the papers are among the most marvelous pieces of misinformation ever read. It is to be said in defense of the credulity of these seekers after the rumored treasure houses that there are holes in the rocks, and crevices in the bluffs, where honey bees have lived for years and each year a certain amount of honey and wax is secured from such locations.

John Taylor Allen alludes to the affluence of honey in the State of Texas: "The wonderful tales told of honey and the honey bee may seem exaggerated but no tale can exaggerate the abundance of honey that was to be found right here in Texas in the early days. What sweet, happy days we had cutting bee trees and eating the rich wild honey spread over our buttered biscuits, . . . We had a bountiful supply the whole year around—combed honey, strained honey and candied honey."

CHAPTER XV

HUNTING FOR WILD HONEY

Painstaking efforts to collect wild honey were just as ancient a sport as hunting and fishing. When the bees were not yet domesticated and nested in hollow trees and rocks, to find the nests and rob them of honey was a profitable and favorite pastime. Special hunters devised all kinds of schemes to ferret out their habitations.

The bees' well-known sense of orientation, as acute as that of homing-pigeons, was an important aid in tracking their lair. Columella (60 A.D.) describes how the hunters followed the bees. Washington Irving (*A Tour of the Prairies,* 1835) gives an account of his experience with honey-hunters in quest of "bee-trees." They placed a honeycomb, which served as bait, on a low bush. Soon the bees appeared and after they had provided themselves with enough honey, they flew into the air and in a "beeline" to their nest. The hunters followed the bees' course and traced them to some hollow tree-trunks where they found their cache sometimes sixty feet above the ground. Then they chopped down the trees and with knives and scoops emptied the cavities, replete with honey. John Burroughs (*Idyl of the Honey-Bee*) described an identical performance.

Tickner Edwardes (*The Bee-Master of Warrilow*) also tells how to discover wild bees' nests. It is useless to search the woods for wild honey, for one may travel a whole day and find nothing. The only plan is to follow the laden bees as they return. The bee-master produces a saucer covered with honey which is in no time black with crowding bees. The saucer is then covered with a wire cage. These captured bees

are the guides to the hidden treasure-chambers. By opening a
small door in the trap, one bee is allowed to escape and she
immediately rises into the air, makes a circle and speeds
away in a certain direction which one must follow. After a
while, another bee is set free, and the same procedure is
repeated until the nest is located high in the hollow of a
dead tree. The Russian name of a beekeeper is "tree-
climber"; in Lithuanian, a "bee-climber." The inseparable
adjunct, almost an emblem of the Hungarian shepherd, is a
stick with a little hatchet on its end. This, called *fokos,*
originally a beekeeper's implement for cutting the trunk of
the tree to remove the welcome treasure. A similar tool is still
used in the District of Hanover, Germany. It is called *Beide*
and is the symbol of beekeeping.

It was a most ancient custom that the finder had the right
to mark the trees with a special design or initials, after which
he or his tribe had the sole privilege of collecting honey from
such trees. The laws were strict and severe punishment was
meted out for altering or destroying these markings. In Germany, if one were caught in the act of trespassing, he had to
pay a fine and, besides, received twenty lashes.

On almost every continent there are birds which are fond
of honey. They show the honey-hunters where the bees' nests
are located. The birds receive their share for these services.
Vasco de Gama related how the "honey-birds" of India
guided the natives to the rocks where honey was to be found.
The *ajaje* birds lead the Lango tribes, and the honey-ratels
the Hottentots to the wild bees' nests. The honey-guide (*Cu-
culus indicator*), a tropical bird, shows the South African
natives where the honey is located. She flies before the
hunters to show them the way. As a reward, the bird receives
part of the spoils. The natives faithfully obey this tradition
and give the birds their liberal share; otherwise, they believe,
out of revenge the birds will surely lead them the next time
to a lion's den or a snake's nest, and then fly away with a
merry chirp. According to a Rhodesian folk-tale, these vindic-
tive creatures lead the travelers to the nests to retaliate for an
old injury which they suffered from the bees.

Among primitive races honey-hunting was an important
event and began with solemn rites. Chastity had to be observed the night before, otherwise the hunters would be badly
stung by the bees or some other misfortune would befall
them.

In the Middle Ages honey-hunting was a royal sport. The German archives describe the Nuremberg forests as a hunting ground of royalty not only for game but for wild honey. Charlemagne began to domesticate wild bees in the Nuremberg forests out of gratitude because, after he had been stung by bees, he recovered from an obstinate gout. The Nuremberg forests were called the bee-garden of the Holy Roman Empire and under the reign of Charles IV (1347), the bee garden of Germany. From the honey collected there, the famous *Lebkuchen* was baked which is still popular the world over after twelve hundred years.

In many countries special permits were issued, and the amount of honey had to be accounted for and taxes paid on it. The Domesday Book mentions that the Bishop of Worcester, under the reign of Edward the Confessor, was privileged to hunt for honey in the forests of Malvern.

The ancient origin of honey-hunting is demonstrated in mythology. The Satyrs (Fauns), the attendants of Dionysus, were extremely fond of honey. In one of the legends the jolly old, red-nosed, bloated and, as a rule, intoxicated Silenus, the schoolmaster and foster-father of Bacchus and the alleged inventor of the flute, was anxious to find the wild bees' nest and plunder it of honey. As the story goes, Silenus stood on his donkey's back, reaching for honey-combs, when the bees flew at him and stung him on his bald head. He fell on top of the donkey, which, when also stung, kicked him and escaped, to the great merriment of the other Satyrs who witnessed his plight. Ovid describes the scene and tells how Dionysus laughed and taught Silenus how to ease the pain of the sting with mud.

Innumerable fables and legends refer to honey-hunting. One of the oldest legends, often mentioned in ancient literature, is that of Antophilus, the Greek poet, who was a great lover of honey and who sang its praise in his poems. Antophilus, while searching for wild honey, climbed a precipice and swinging on a rope, emptied the contents of a nest. Some honey trickled down the rope. His dog, also very fond of honey, chewed the rope and Antophilus fell from the perilous height and was killed.

The following, a rather amusing little story from Poland, is credited to Demetrius, the Russian Ambassador to Rome: "A man, searching in the woods for honey, slipped down into a great hollow tree, where he found himself up to his breast in a veritable lake of this sweet substance. He stuck fast there for two days, making the lonely woods resound in vain with his cries for help. Finally, when the man had almost abandoned hope, a large bear appeared upon the scene, bent on the same business that had taken the man there. Bruin smelled the honey, which had been stirred up by the struggles of the prisoner, and straightway climbed the tree and let himself down backward into the hollow. The man, whose wits had been sharpened by the adversity, caught him about the loins and made as vigorous an outcry as he could. Up clambered Bruin in a panic, not knowing what had got hold of him. Our man clung fast, and the bear tugged, until by main force he had pulled himself and his captor out of the tree; then he let go and Bruin, considerably frightened, took to the woods with all speed, leaving his smeared companion to his own congratulations." Wilhelm Busch, the graphic humorist and pastmaster of comical sequence, must have been quite impressed by the story since he illustrated it with a complete serial of pictures.

In connection with honey-hunting we find among the primitive tribes of far-off continents many fanciful tales which relate the identical and characteristic yarn. The honey-hunter usually finds among the honeycombs in a tree an enchanted *bee-woman* who will cook for him and will prepare a delicious honey-wine. The hunter proposes marriage to her, which she accepts under the condition that he should never mention to anybody where he had found her, otherwise, she would disappear. This actual proviso is typical also of many other myths; the story of Psyche, the Lohengrin Saga and the story of Undine, are only a few instances. This peculiar secrecy seems to be analogous, in certain respects, with the curious marriage customs of primitive races, according to which a wife was not permitted to pronounce the husband's name or it was unlawful for a husband to see his wife's face until after she had given birth to her first child.

The following is a popular legend along the Orinoco River (Amazon region): There was a man who possessed great skill in detecting bees' nests, with which the forest abounded; in fact, he was better in this respect than anyone else. One day the man tried to drill a hollow tree, with the intention of removing honey, when suddenly he heard a loud scream, "You are killing me!" He carefully opened the tree and to his amazement, saw a beautiful naked woman before him. He made her a loin-cloth and bade her marry him. The woman consented to be his wife under one condition, that he would never call her Maba (bee), or tell anyone that it was her name. Our man promised and the two became husband and wife. The hunter remained just as efficient in finding the bees' nests as in former days. His wife made the best honey-wine that was ever brewed; a cupful was sufficient to supply all the guests. On one occasion, many visitors arrived, and they all became intoxicated. The host promised his guests that the next time his wife would prepare more and still better honey-wine, and in the same breath referred to her as Maba. In an instant, like a shot, Maba flew away. From that time on the man's luck changed and honey became scarce in the region. His wife had been one of the legendary bee-women.

There are similar tales in Indonesia. The Bornean version, quoted in *The Mythology of All Races* (Vol. IX), is as follows:

A man named Rakian was out hunting for honey, when in the top of a mangis tree he saw many bees' nests, in one of which were white bees. (Several Christian legends allude to snow-white bees producing virginal honey.) Since white bees were a rarity, he carefully removed the nest and took it home. The next day he was working in his garden and when he returned to his house in the evening he found a meal cooked for him. He was surprised because he lived alone. The following day the same thing occurred, his meal was again cooked. This continued for some time. Finally he resolved to investigate the mystery.

He pretended to go to the garden but silently returned, hid himself and watched. The door of the house soon creaked and a beautiful woman came out, and went to the river to fetch some water. While she was gone, Rakian entered the house, and found that the bees' nest was empty. He hid the nest and secreted himself again. The woman returned and upon finding the nest gone commenced to weep. In the evening Rakian entered the house as was his custom. The woman sat there silent. "Why are you here?" he asked, "perhaps you want to steal my bees?" The woman answered, "I don't know anything about your bees." Rakian asked her to cook for him because he was hungry, but she refused, as she was vexed. The woman demanded her box but he was afraid that she would disappear into it again. She promised not to, and that she would become his wife if he would not disclose her identity. Rakian agreed; they were married and by and by she bore him a child.

One day Rakian went to a feast at his neighbors. All asked him whence his beautiful wife had come. He evaded the question. After a while, when they all were intoxicated, he forgot his promise and revealed to his friends that his wife had been a bee.

When he returned, his wife did not speak to him. Later she reproached him for having broken his promise and said that she must return to her home. "In seven days my father will pass here and I shall go with him, but the child I leave with you." Rakian wept. He could not change her mind. Seven days later he saw a white bee flying by, whereupon his wife came out of the house and exclaimed: "There is my father." She turned into a bee and flew away.

Rakian picked up the child and pursued the bees. For seven days he followed them until finally he lost sight of them. Soon a strange woman appeared who directed him to his wife's home. Rakian climbed into the house and found it full of bees, except the middle room. The child began to cry, when suddenly Rakian's wife appeared. Rakian was happy but she reproached him for revealing her secret. Finally they became reconciled and all the bees dropped down from the roof-beams to the floor and became men. Rakian and the child remained in the bees' village.

There are similar fables among the African tribes.

An old Hungarian fable suggests that Christ, Himself, was a honey-hunter. Christ and St. Peter were wandering. Peter said, "It must be wonderful to be a God, help the widows and orphans, reward good deeds and punish the wicked. If this could be accomplished, there wouldn't be any vice on earth." While Peter was talking, Jesus looked around and noticed a bees' nest in the hollow of a tree. Christ suggested to Peter that he put the swarm into his cap, "Maybe they will be useful." Peter obeyed and put cluster after cluster into his cap until one of the bees stung him on the finger. With a loud cry of pain, he threw the cap, full of bees, to the ground, saying, "Oh, the devil shall take this swarm; how one of them has stung me!" Christ said, "Well, why don't you find the one which stung you?" "How can I," said Peter, "they all look alike." Then Jesus said, "If you were God, you would do the same thing; if one of your people sinned, all the innocent would have to suffer."

During the pioneer days of America honey-hunting was a

profitable pursuit and a favorite occupation of the Southwestern backwoodsmen. Wild honey was sold for a quarter of a
dollar a gallon and some bee-trees yielded as much as a
dozen gallons of honey. The honey-hunter with his old som-
brero, open hickory shirt and deer-skin breeches is often
described in contemporary writings. He is portrayed as a real
character; fond of nature, solitude and the stillness of the
woods, listening to the drowsy hum of the bees. His power of
vision became extremely keen through education and he
could follow the bees with his eyes for hundreds of yards.
His equipment consisted of an axe, several buckets, a fishing
outfit and, of course, a rifle to protect him from Indians and
bears.

The honey hunters, as a rule, built their log-cabins near
navigable rivers and grew their vegetables on the land surrounding their shacks. They depended on their rifles to procure the necessary meat. Honey was an important article of
barter. After the hunters had collected several barrels of
honey, they rolled them down to the river bank, placed them
on boats, and paddled their cargo to the nearest settlement
where they exchanged the honey for flour, gunpowder, lead
and other necessities. Hunters who lived on or near the banks
of the Mississippi traded their honey with the skippers of the
steamboats. The rivermen took the honey to New Orleans,
where they sold it at a fair profit.

The importance of felling bee trees is best proven by the
dispute which occurred in 1840 between the States of Iowa
and Missouri. A farmer of Clark County (Mo.) cut down
several bee trees filled with honey on the boundary line
between the two States. This strip of land had been claimed
by both States and ended in the so-called *Honey-War*. The
United States Supreme Court finally decided the matter in
1851 and settled the exact boundary between the two States.

CHAPTER XVI

HONEY IN RELIGION

A mong polytheistic nations (Varro counted 30,000 gods), sacrifices to the gods were a common practice. These oblational services consisted of prayers supplemented with gifts, to win the favor of the gods and to express gratitude for their bounty or to appease their anger and ward off their sinister influence; in a word, sacrifices to the gods were either thank offerings or sin offerings. The hunters sacrificed their prey, the farmers their fruit and harvest products or animals, like horses, bulls, sheep, etc. In some countries, occasionally even women and children were sacrificed.

We find that honey was universally used in consecratory rites when people wished to offer something especially holy and acceptable to a deity as an expression of thanksgiving, penitence or atonement. Sophocles in the fragment of the lost *Polydos* describes the offerings, dear to the gods:

> "Wool of the sheep was there, fruit of the vine,
> Libations and the treasured store of grapes.
> And manifold fruits were there, mingled with grain
> And oil of olive, and fair curious combs
> Of wax, compacted by the yellow bee."

To the ancient Germanic god, Neckar, there was yearly sacrificed a man, a sheep, a loaf of bread and a beehive.

Honey, the celestial food, collected from the "virtues" of flowers, was considered by all ancients the symbol of purity, love and wisdom. During the Leontic (inhabitants of an ancient Greek town in the province of Syracuse) initiation ceremonies honey was poured on the hands, instead of water, to keep them pure from everything that causes pain, harm or brings defilement. Honey was also thought to purify the tongue from every sin. St. Gregory (Pope, 590–604 A.D.), in *Morals on the Book of Job* (Vol. II, p. 185), remarked, "When the grace of the Holy Spirit bathes us, it fills us with honey and butter equally. Honey falls from above, butter is drawn from the milk of animals, so honey is from the air, butter from the flesh." In primitive baptism the neophyte drank a cup of milk and honey mixed; "the new-born in Christ" partook of the food of infants. St. Jerome mentions among the "unsanctioned rites" the cup of honey and milk. While honey was used in the early Christian services, by the end of the sixth century its use in the Roman church was discontinued. The Copts and Ethiopians, however, kept it up in their baptismal ceremonies. The wine used in Ethiopia for communion purposes is prepared from honey. Honey, in all probability, symbolized the Land of Promise. The fifth century book, *Joseph and Arsenath*, relates how the angel had eaten a piece of honeycomb and also put a piece into the mouth of Arsenath, exclaiming, "Now thou hast eaten the bread of life and hast drunk the cup of immortality and received the unction of incorruption." In Persia during the Mithraic feasts honey was used on the hands of the candidates as a cleansing substance instead of water. The Christians ate honey before fast-days, especially on Holy Thursday. On the eve of the Jewish New Year an apple dipped in honey was eaten; fruit and honey symbolized prosperity and peace.

Prehistoric man worshiped the sun, the most glorious object in Nature, as the supreme god, the giver and sustainer of all life. Only the most intellectual amongst the primitive races were sun-worshipers. Honey had a significant part in all their rituals. The Babylonians and Assyrians poured honey on the foundation-stones and walls of the temples. Nebuchadnezzar was a liberal user of honey. The priests anointed themselves with honey and placed some on the altars. At sunrise honey sacrifices were brought to the Sun-God. In one of the Magical papyri (Berlin), the worshiper is thus instructed: "Take honey with the milk, drink it before the rising of the sun, and there shall be in thy heart something that is divine." We find that the same custom existed among the Egyptians and among the Incas of Peru. The Hindus and

Persians used honey in profusion during their religious services; they considered honey a sacred substance, a divine food,
a cleanser and purifier.

Many rituals of the African tribes in Somaliland, Galla-
land, and also of the Bushmen and Hottentots, even today,
are intimately associated with honey. The Hottentots dance
during full moon and pray for plenty of honey and milk.
Their honey harvests are opened with religious ceremonies.
No one is allowed to collect honey before a certain time. The
priests taste the honey first and then they announce that
everyone is permitted to collect his share. In medieval France
pilgrimages were conducted to certain shrines to pray for an
abundant honey harvest.

There are many evidences in ancient archives which prove
the importance of bees and of their products, honey and wax,
in the Christian religion. The Lorsch (Hessen, Germany)*
manuscript in the Vatican library is an interesting example. It
is a supplication to the Lord to protect the bees, these "dear
animals," *vihu minaz.* The huge bronze baldachin before the
main altar of St. Peter's Church in Rome is studded with
bees, likewise the tomb of Urban VIII. The shape of the
papal tiara was unquestionably derived from an old-fashioned
beehive (skep). On the title-page picture of the German edition of *De roomische byen-korf* (Roman beehive), by Filips
van Marnix, the papal tiara serves as a hive for the bees. One
bee represents the pope (king bee), others function as cardi-
nals, bishops and monks saying Mass and attending to burials
and confessions. According to a passage of the book, "our
dear and loving mother, the holie church of Rome, ought not
to scorn or disdaine that we do compare her customs and
orders to a Bee-Hive, considering that shee herself doth
compare the incomprehensible generation of the Sonne of
God from his Father, together with his birth out of the pure
and undefiled Virgine Marie unto the Bees; which were in
verie deede a great blasphemie, if the bees were not of so
great vertue, that by them wee might liken and compare the
holie church of Rome. And, seeing, she saith, that God is
delighted with the giftes and presentes of the bees, why
should not shee herself exceedingly rejoyce with our Bee-
Hive."†

---

* Lorsch was one of the localities where Charlemagne kept his bees.
† Quoted by W. Hone, *Ancient Mysteries*, 1823.

EXULTET ROLLS

A most notable acknowledgment of the significance of bees and honey is found in the Exultet Rolls. These sumptuously illustrated liturgical parchment manuscripts, some of them twenty-two feet long and one foot in breadth, are the oldest extant texts of the Roman Mass. They date back to the early eleventh century and were named after the first word of the prayer, *Exultet iam angelica turba caelorum* (Let now rejoice the heavenly choir of angels). It was sung by the monks on Easter Eve during the consecration of the Easter taper. The texts are divided into short chapters, intersected by elaborately illuminated pictures. The pictures are in reverse to the text so that, when the priests chanted the songs and unfolded the rolls over the pulpit, the congregation could see the subject illustrated. Certain sections of these prayers are veritable eulogies of bees and honey. "Talia igitur Domine, digna sacris altaribus tuis munera offeruntur, quibus te laetari religio Christiana non ambigit." (Such gifts, therefore, O Lord, are offered worthy of thy altars, with which the Christian religion does not hesitate that thou rejoicest.)

The Barberini manuscript in the Vatican library is a typical specimen. In a garden of flowery bushes, with trees in the center, bees, gathering honey, cover the entire field. A crouching bee-master cuts honeycombs from the hive and places them in a bowl. Another figure is holding a pitcher under it, not to waste a drop of honey. Two other men are cutting the branch of a tree to hive a swarm which settled on it. The rolls of Monte Cassino, Capua, Troja, Fondi, Gaeta, Bari, Mirabella, etc., vary in composition but all are decorated with hives and laboring bees.

IN THE BIBLE

Honey is frequently mentioned in the Bible; it was referred to as a wholesome food, a helpful medicine, an ingredient of delicious drinks, an appropriate gift and a valued possession. There is only little evidence that the Hebrews cultivated bees, but they used wild honey in profusion. "Wild" honey is often mentioned; whether this was meant as a contrast to domesticated honey, it is difficult to say. That the Jews were solicitous about their honey supply is indicated in the Talmud (B. Batra 18, A) where a warning is given never to let mustard plants grow near bees' nests because bees are fond of these flowers which, however, burn their throats and they then consume a greater quantity of honey. The Jews were permitted, according to their religious laws, to provide water on Saturdays and holidays to their domestic animals, but this dispensation did not apply to bees, because they themselves could secure it (Sabath 24:3). On the other hand, in case of rain, or to protect the bees from the scorching sun, the Jews were permitted to cover the nests with linen even on holidays (Sabath 436).

Philo, the historian (in the time of Christ), in his work, *De Vita Contemplativa* (II. 663), refers to a caste among the Hebrews called Essenes, who lived in the region of the Dead Sea, and whose occupation was supposed to be the cultivation of bees and the production of honey. Josephus, in the *Antiquities of the Jews*, also mentions the Essenes of Judea. (It is noteworthy that the Greek term Essenos [king bee] was the epithet of Zeus. The priestesses of Artemis were called Melissai [bees] and their high priests, Essenes.)

When the Hebrews referred to Palestine they used the proverbial metaphor, expressive of plenty, "a land flowing with milk and honey." This reference is repeated twenty-one times in the Bible. (Exod. 3: 8; 3: 17; 13: 5; 33: 3; Lev. 30: 35; Num. 13: 28; 14: 8; 16: 14; Deut. 6: 3; 11: 9; 26: 15; 27: 3; 31: 20; Jos. 5: 6; Tob. 30: 17; Jer. 11: 5; 32: 22; Ezek. 20: 6; 30: 15; Sirach 46, 10; Baruch 1, 20.) The day Christ rose from the dead and appeared before His Disciples, He asked for food. They gave Him broiled fish and a honeycomb (Luke 24: 42). Christ ate the food to prove to the Apostles that He was truly resurrected and not merely a Spirit or a Thought. John the Baptist, in his camel's hair raiment, ate dried locusts and honey in the wilderness (Mark 1: 6, Matth. 3: 4). In the Hebrew language *debash* means honey and Deborah, bee.

There was honey galore in Palestine. Samuel described woods where honey was so plentiful that the combs were strewn on the ground. "And when the people were come into the woods, behold, the honey dropped." (Samuel 14: 26.) Not only trees but also the rocks poured forth honey. "He would feed them . . . with honey out of the rock." In the songs of Moses there is an allusion, "he shall not see the rivers, the flowing streams of honey and butter." (Job 20: 17.) Prophet Isaiah (eighth century B.C.) mentions honey and butter:

". . . for butter and honey shall everyone eat that is left in the midst of the land." (Isa. 7: 21.)

The heaven-born manna, on which the Israelites subsisted in the desert for forty years, contained honey; it was probably honey-dew. "And the House of Israel called the name thereof manna; and it resembled coriander seed, white, and tasted like wafers made with honey." (Exod. 16: 31.) That manna contained only a small quantity of honey is mentioned in the chapter of the "Fives" in the Talmud:

> "Fire is one-sixtieth of hell,
> Honey is one-sixtieth of manna,
> Sabbath one-sixtieth of rest of the world to come,
> Sleep one-sixtieth of death,
> Dreams one-sixtieth of prophecy."

Honey must have been an important article of commerce among the Jews. Ezekiel mentions (27: 17) that the Israelites, in addition to wine, oil and balsams, also carried honey to a Phoenician mercantile town, known as Tyrus, and it is possible that they supplied other markets with honey. That the Jews put aside honey for future use is proven by the appeal of the men to Ishmael: "Slay us not, for we have stores hidden in the fields, of wheat and of barley and of oil and of honey." (Jer. 41: 8.)

There are many references in the Bible to honey as an attractive gift. Jacob, the Patriarch, when he sent his son to Egypt, gave him honey, spices, myrrh and almonds to deliver as a present to the Governor. When Jeroboam's queen visited the blind Prophet Ahijah at Shiloh (Kings 14: 3), she brought with her a cruse of honey in order to obtain a favorable report about her dying son. Possibly honey was also intended to cure the Prophet's blindness. King David's army, 3,000 years ago, was provided with honey, . . . "they brought beds and basins and earthen vessels and wheat and barley . . . beans and lentils . . . and honey and butter for David and for the people with him, to eat; for they said, the people are hungry and weary and thirsty in the wilderness." (2 Sam. 17: 28, 29.) That the Hebrews highly valued honey as a food substance is conclusively proven by the words of the son of Sirach, who recognized honey as "one of the principal things for use in man's life." (Eccl. 39: 26.) The medicinal value of honey is often emphasized in the Talmud.

It was used for various diseases, especially for heart troubles, gout and as an external application for the wounds of man and beast. Mixing honey with wine is repeatedly mentioned. Assyria was called the land of honey and olive trees.

Honey was frequently employed in the Bible in a symbolical sense, namely, to draw a comparison between some act or conception and the sweetness of honey. David, who had been a shepherd boy, often utilized metaphorically the sweetness of honey: "The judgment of the Lord is sweeter than honey and the droppings of the honeycomb." (Ps. 19: 10.) "How sweet are thy words to my taste, yea, sweeter than honey in my mouth." (Ps. 119: 102.) In Solomon's Proverbs (16: 24): "Pleasant words are as an honeycomb, sweet to the soul and health to the bones." "The lips of the bride are as sweet as honey. The lips of the concubine are like honey but later bitter as vermuth" (Prov. 5:3). There are two accounts in the Bible of men being ordered to eat a book and in each case "the book tasted as sweet as honey." (Ezek. 3: 3 and Revel. 10: 9, 10.) In the Revelation: "And I took the little book out of the angel's hand, and ate it up; and it was in my mouth sweet as honey."

The mythical tale of Samson (Judges 14:5-18) is well known. Samson was calling on his Philistine sweetheart when he was attacked by a young lion. Samson had no weapon, only the Spirit of Jehovah came mightily upon him and "he rent the lion as he would have rent a kid." When he returned "after a while" he passed the spot and found that bees had taken possession of the lion's carcass and had built combs in it, where they stored their honey. Samson removed some honey, took it home, gave a portion to his father and to his mother and ate some of it himself.

During his marriage feast Samson put a riddle to the Philistine young men: "Out of the eater came forth meat and out of the strong came forth sweetness." The young men could not solve the riddle for three days, but Samson's wife obtained from him the answer and betrayed him to the young men, who then claimed to have solved the enigma by saying: "What is sweeter than honey and what is stronger than a lion?"

This Biblical tale was much discussed by ancient and modern apicultural writers. Aristotle emphasized the bees' dislike for strong odors and decayed matter. It seems improbable that the bees would utilize a carcass for their nesting place.

On the other hand, it must be taken into consideration that in tropical countries at a certain season of the year the heat is so intense that it dries up all moisture and the carcass will not undergo decomposition. In the desert dead camels remain mummified for a long time and their bodies are entirely free from offensive odors. Often jackals, vultures and dogs gnaw off the soft parts and only the skeleton remains in which the bees may build their combs. In the West of the United States (Montana) skeletons of oxen have been found which the bees had converted into dwelling places.

Honey sacrifices were prohibited by the Jews as honey was liable to ferment. "Ye shall burn no leaven, nor any honey as an offering unto Jehovah" (Lev. 2: 11). Honey, however, was allowed as a "not burnt" offering or as a tribute of first fruit (Lev. 2: 12). One may assume that the Jews used honey as a leavening for baking purposes.

Today, there is again honey in abundance in modern Palestine and vigorous efforts have been made by the inhabitants to find foreign markets for their bees and honey.

CHAPTER XVII

HONEY IN MYTHOLOGIES

Honey, honey cake and honey drinks played an important part in all mythologies. Ambrosia (honey and milk) was the food of the Greek and Roman gods and the celestial Nectar, the drink of Mount Olympus. The nectar of the gods, compounded of fermented honey and spices, was considered a delicious and salubrious drink and was poured by Hebe and Ganymede, the cupbearers of Zeus. It was reputed to impart a divine bloom, beauty and vigor to those who were so fortunate as to obtain it. Nectar possessed wondrous life-giving properties, the power to prevent decay and corruption and secure immortality.

Ambrosia, according to Porphyry (*The Cave of the Nymphs*), was nine times as nourishing as honey. Nectar was really mead. Plato mentions (*Symp.*, p. 203), how Poros fell asleep in the garden of Zeus, drunk not with wine but with nectar because wine "was not yet." Plutarch also remarks (*Symp.* IV. 6.) that mead was used as a libation before wine appeared and adds, "even now, those barbarians who do not drink wine, drink mead." Martial compared the nectar of the gods to Falernian wine, mixed with Attic honey.

Zeus, the omnipresent, omniscient and omnipotent father of the gods, was brought up on honey. According to the legend, the father of Zeus, Cronos, one of the Titans, married his own sister, Rhea. Cronos ate his children as soon as they were born because it was presaged that one of his offspring would replace him in the heavenly kingdom. Cronos had already devoured the five elder children. Zeus, the sixth and most beautiful of them, was hidden by his mother after his

birth in an almost inaccessible grotto in Mt. Ida, on the
island of Crete. Rhea wrapped a stone in swaddling bands,
which looked like a newborn child, and gave it to Cronos,
who swallowed it, thinking that it was his son. The daughters
of the King, the nymphs Melitta (the bee) and Amalthea (the
goat), nursed Zeus on honey and milk. When Zeus grew up
he dethroned his father after a ten years' war and became the
ruler of Mt. Olympus. The number of legendary tales asso-
ciating Zeus with bees and honey are infinite. Homer gave
Zeus the epithet, Essenos, the Bee King. On many ancient
Greek coins there is a head of Zeus and on the reverse side, a
bee. Honey was considered a heavenly gift. Zeus rained
honey (honeydew) which had the power to raise the dead.
Plutarch called honey the saliva of the stars (*salivo siderum*).

The Hindus believed that the heaven-born honey which
fell on the leaves and grass sweetened even the milk of cows
and goats. Kalidasa in the *"Hero and Nymph"* exclaims:

> "Delightful words! they fell like drops of nectar,
> No wonder nectar from the moon should flow."

In Hindu mythology the moon had the epithet, *Madhukara*,
honey-giver.

Artemis, the Moon-goddess, was often figured in the shape
of a bee. It was an ancient Germanic belief that the moon
was supposed to be a huge cup, filled with honey and mead;
and the stars were swarms of bees, whose honey fell to the
earth upon the oak and sweet ash. The honeydew which
settled over the mighty sacred ash, Ygdrasil (representing the
tree of the Universe), nourished the bees. The well of Ymir,
the source of all wisdom, was under this tree and Odin
pawned one of his eyes to obtain a drink from it.

The sweet ash which was believed to feed the bees with
honeydew had noteworthy significance in all mythologies.
The word ash (in Latin melia, mel=honey) is derived from
the Norse *aska*, meaning, man. Odin fashioned the first man
from this tree. Pliny mentioned that all evil creatures have a
fear of the ash and that serpents would rather pass through
fire than over its leaves. Mothers used to place the cradles of
their infants under an ash tree to protect them from harm.
The Finnish shepherds planted an ash stick on the pasture to
protect their cattle and the Scotch Highlanders placed a
piece of the wood over their cow stables to keep the witches

from contaminating the milk. Achilles used an ashen spear and Cupid made his arrows from ash.

The Bushmen call honey *moon's water*. When the game is shot and does not die, or even arises, they believe it is due to the magic effect of moon's water. The Bushmen have a special drum called *goin-goin* and while they are beating it they dance and pray that the bees may become abundant and bring home honey, so that their women and children will not go hungry.

There is much evidence in all mythologies of how fond the gods were of honey. Ovid relates in *Metamorphosis* that Jupiter and Mercury were traveling through Phrygia as plain mortals and no one would admit them, except two charitable souls living in a modest tent, who offered them the food which they most desired, namely, honey, milk and fruit.

Eros (Amor) was often pictured as a honey-thief. Anacreon, the Greek bard (fifth century B.C.), has written an immortal song, *Eros, the honey-thief*. Theocritus (third century B.C.) transcribed the same poem, *Love stealing honey*. Lucas Cranach, the distinguished early sixteenth century painter, composed no less than nine pictures of Amor as a honey-thief. Albrecht Dürer made the drawing of his *Honey-Thief* in 1514. Many antique gems depict Amor in association with honey. One of them represents Amor floating over waves with spread sails on a honey jar on which there is the image of a bee. On another gem Amor, to protect the bees, chases some birds from a tree. Amor is supposed to have dipped his arrows into honey to produce blissful love. He was often called metaphorically the honey-bird, with "eyes and voice as sweet as honey." In the *Idyl of Moschus*, the Greek bucolic poet of Syracuse (200 B.C.), Venus thus describes the lost Cupid, whom she is trying to find: "The child is most notable; thou couldst tell him among twenty others; his skin is not white but flame colored; his eyes are keen and burning; an evil heart and a honeyed tongue has he, for his speech and mind are at variance. Like honey is his voice but his heart of gall; all tameless is he and deceitful, the truth is not in him, a wily brat and cruel in his pastime."

It is interesting that Kama, the Hindu god of love, is also closely associated with honey and bees. Kama rides on a bee* and the string of his bow consists of a chain of bees, symbol-

---

* On a Hittite gem found near Aleppo, Atargatis (another name for Diana of Ephesus, originating in Babylon) stands on a bee.

izing the sweetness and sting of love. (Honey and the sting of
the bee are contrasted as often as roses and thorns.) Kalidasa,
the Hindu poet, refers to Kama and his bow. For instance, in
The Birth of the War-God, Kama:

> "Weaves a string of bees with deft invention
>   To speed the missile when the bow is bent."

Then again in the *Shakuntala:*

> "A stalwart soldier comes, the spring,
>   Who bears the bow of Love;
> And on that bow, the lustrous *string*
>   Is made of bees. . . ."

Possibly the names of the two gods, Amor and Kama, were
derived from the same root, *amo,* I love.

The Hindus, Greeks, Romans and all Slavic races had gods
for bees and honey. There were only a few gods in mythologies to whom honey sacrifices were not offered. Zeus, Ceres,
her daughter, honied Proserpina, Apollo, Dionysus, Aphrodite, even Hecate of Hades were some of the gods to whom
frequent honey offerings were brought. Dionysus was also
worshiped as a honey-god. His priestesses carried in their
hands the thyrsos, a cane with a crown of ivy. Euripides
comments, "the ivy wands distilled from all their tops rich
store of honey."

> "And as they pass, through every plain
> Flows milk, flows wine, the nectar'd honey flows,
> And round each soft gale Syrian odors throws."

Virgil, in *Georgics I,* refers to the honey sacrifices brought
to Ceres: "For thee let all the rural youths adore Ceres; to
whom mix thou the honeycomb with milk and gentle wine."

In one of his *Elegies,* Tibullus describes the honey offerings to the household gods:

> "Or dulcet cakes himself the farmer paid,
> When crown'd his wishes by your powerful aid;
> While his fair daughter brought with her from home
> The luscious offering of a honeycomb."

Empedocles (490–430 B.C.) mentions the honey sacrifices
to Aphrodite:

"And holy offerings of unmixed myrrh,
And sweetly smelling frankincense; and many
A pure libation of fresh golden honey
They pour'd along the floor."

According to the legend, Dedalus, the divine artist and the builder of the famous Cretan labyrinth, made a honeycomb for Aphrodite from the purest gold which looked so natural that it was confused with a real one. (Diodorus Siculus IV. 78.)

Pan,* the god of shepherds, Priapus, the god of gardens, and the Nymphs were considered the protectors of the bees and they had also their share of honey offerings. In one of the *Idyls* of Theocritus, the shepherd professes: "And I will set out eight bowls of milk for Pan and eight bowls, full of the richest honeycombs."

Many priestesses and nymphs, according to Greek mythology, gained their inspiration from honey intoxicants under the influence of which "they raved in holy frenzy." Horace refers to it in the *"Ode to Bacchus"*:

"Give me to sing, by thee inspir'd,
Thy priestesses to madness fir'd:
Fountains of wine shall pour along,
And, melting from the hollow tree,
The golden treasures of the bee,
And streams of milk shall fill the song."

Homer in the *"Hymn to Mercury"* comments on the prophetic powers with which the priestesses were endowed by indulging in honey drinks:

"From these I have learned true
Vaticinations of remotest things
My father cared not. Whilst they search out dooms,
They sit apart and feed on honey-combs.
Drunk with divine enthusiasm, and utter
With earnest willingness the truth they know,
But, if deprived of that sweet food, they mutter
All plausible delusions;—these to you
I give;—if you inquire, they will not stutter;
Delight your own soul with them;—any man
You would instruct may profit if he can."

---

* The word panic was derived from mischievous Pan, who took delight in frightening unsuspecting travelers.

The hypnotic effect of honey is frequently mentioned in mythology. Orpheus sang that if anyone fell asleep after eating honey it was difficult to awaken him. Zeus, before he attacked his father, put him asleep with a honey drink:

"When prostrate 'neath the lofty oaks you see him
Lie drunken with the work of murmuring bees,
Then bind him. . . ."
Porphyry (*De antr. nymph.* 7)

Virgil relates that when his hero Aeneas descended to Hades, he flung a soporific honey cake to Cerberus and that the creature "in a mad rage opened his three mouths and snatched the offered morsel, relaxing his monstrous limbs, extending a vast length all over the cave." Three times each year honey sacrifices were offered to Pluto, the god of the underworld. The Romans had divers names for their religious places. One was called *scrobiculus.* It consisted of a pit containing an altar on which they poured the blood of a slain beast tempered with honey as a sacrifice to the infernal deity. To *Bona Dea* (the Earth), a mixture of milk and honey was offered and the container in which it was kept was called the *honey-vessel.* Chaucer in *The Knight's Tale:*

"With vessels in her hand of gold full fine,
All full of Hony, Milk, Blood and Wine."

Plutarch mentions (*Symp.* 5) that the Athenians offered no wine to their gods but only water, sweetened with honey.

To the Fates who spin the thread of human destiny, honey was also offered. The Spartan women believed that the Fates, though invisible, frequently visited a newborn child, especially on the third or fifth night after birth. They left the doors of the house open on these nights and set on the table bread, honey and water to win the favor of the Fates.

The use of honey cake as a sacrificial offering was universal in all mythologies. In Egypt the sacred bull Apis and the sacred crocodile of Thebes were fed on honey cakes. It was an ancient custom in Egypt to consult in all perplexing situations the sacred bull at the oracle of Memphis. Food was offered to Apis; if this was accepted, it was considered a favorable sign, if refused, it was an indication of ill-omen. As an inducement, to tickle the palate of Apis, the food was mixed with honey to secure a propitious ruling.

Among the Greeks, Romans, the Germanic and Slavic races sacrificial offering of honey cake was an established and favorite ceremony.

In the *Rig-Veda* honey was a super-eminent subject. Vishnu, Indra and Krishna were all called *Madhava*, honey-born. The two demigods, Aswins, who attended to the welfare of men, were the children of the Sun and the Moon, the givers of dawn, of a new day. They were pictured in a three-wheeled golden chariot, on which they carried honey. Many hymns were sung to the Aswins: "Harness your bounty-shedding golden chariot with swift horses, refresh our strength with trickling honey, bring prosperity to our people and to our cattle. Animate us, prolong our existence, bring us vigor, wipe out our sins, destroy our foes and be always with us." The Hindus prayed at daybreak to the Aswins, the creators of a new day:

"Anoint me with the honey of the bee,
That I may speak forceful speech among men,"

The Russians and all the Slavs had honey-gods, and images of these deities were only seldom missing in their gardens.

Jovial (Jove) feasts, carnal pleasures and boisterous revelries, characterized by overindulgence in food and intemperate drinking, were the daily amusement of the heathen deities. Without intoxicating beverages this could not be imagined. Wine, whisky, and beer did not exist in those days, and drinks made from honey were used instead.

Mead (derived from the Hindu word madhu, honey), the drink of the Norse gods, was the nectar of Mt. Olympus. Odin, the chief of the Norsemen, patron of wisdom, culture and heroes, visited Saga, the Goddess of History, and drank mead with her out of a golden goblet.

Odin was supposed to have orginated in Scythia and to have subdued with his tribes the whole of Northern Europe. He later became the Anglo-Saxon Woden and the Wotan of the Niebelungen. Odin, after his birth, was exposed as a helpless child. He was stabbed and hung on a tree. Ymir freed him, healed his wounds and gave him some mead from the Wonder-Kettle of Oedroerir, which renewed his strength. But once Odin had tasted mead, he sacrificed his life to obtain the vessel. Odin gave the meal, which was put before him, to his wolves; mead alone was ample food and drink for him.

Odin and all his followers loved mead which they drank from their horns:

> "Went there at times a fair maid round the board,
>   upfilling the mead-horns,—
> Blush'd she with downcast eyne,—in the mirrowing
>   shield her image,
> Even as she blush'd too;—how it gladded the
>   deep-drinking champions!"

Odin's principal pleasures were carnage, war, banquets, the "celestial" boar and mead, which virgins served to him in the skulls of his enemies. It is singular that in Scandinavian languages the word "Skol" (skull) is used when they drink to the health of people. It, undoubtedly, originated from the legend of Odin.

> "Their banquet is the mighty chine
> Exhaustless, the stupendous boar;
> Virgins of immortal line
> Present the goblet foaming o'er;
> Of heroes' skulls the goblet made
> With figur'd deaths and snakes of gold inlaid."

Penrose thus opens the *Carousal of Odin:*

> "Fill the honey'd bev'rage high,
> Fill the skulls, 'tis Odin's cry!
> Heard ye not the powerful call,
> Thundering through the vaulted hall?
> Fill the meath and spread the board,
> Vassals of the grisly lord!—
> The feast begins, the skull goes round,
> Laughter shouts—the shouts resound."

The Valkyries took the dead heroes to Valhalla, the slain warriors' Paradise, where under a golden roof they continued to live in celestial glory. From the udders of the goat, Hei-drun, savory mead was supposed to flow; "From out her teats there runneth forth so much mead that she filleth therewith each day a huge drinking vessel and all are made drunken thereby." (Gudrun mixed her mead with the blood of her spouse.) The meth was inexhaustible, like the celestial boar, which was eaten by day and restored by night.

Alaric and Attila, the descendants of Odin, also favored mead.

> "Bid him welcome, maiden; haste,
> Let him our metheglin taste."

That it sometimes led to mischief we may see in the *Elder Edda*:

> "For Asi sons the bowl I fill
> With mead, the source of many an ill."

It is possible that Attila, the Scourge of God, when he married the beautiful Ildiko (about 452 A.D.) and died from nose-bleed during the wedding festivities, had indulged in too much mead. When Ossian, the Gaelic poet (third century), referred to a liquor, "the joy and strength of shells," which so delighted his heroes, he probably meant mead. Shells were used by many ancient races as drinking vessels, e.g., the Caledonians. Their descendants in some parts of the Highlands still use them today. The expression "Feast of Shells" alludes to this custom.

In Nordic mythology, derived from the Eddas, honey is often mentioned. In Finnish mythology, the bees were implored to fly to the sun and moon, into the dwelling of the Creator; to carry honey and health in their mouths and on their wings to the good, and wounds of fire and iron to the wicked.

Bees were supposed to have made honey in Paradise and to be survivors of the Golden Age (which preceded the present state of vice and misery), when there was no need for worry, and happy simplicity for men and beasts prevailed.

CHAPTER XVIII

HONEY IN TRADITIONS, CUSTOMS
AND SUPERSTITIONS

In all ages honey, and indirectly its producer, the bee, were closely connected with the domestic life of the populace, and thus had a profound, almost magnetic influence on the people. The conception of honey was associated with everything that was holy, agreeable and beneficial.

The origin of these traditions and customs is almost impossible to trace. They were handed down from one generation to another, for innumerable centuries. Though some traditions have certain national characteristics, most of them were not limited to defined territories, but were disseminated among nations far apart. The same popular customs are found among the Far Eastern, Asiatic, African and European races and the distances which they traveled, compared to our present day facilities of communication, must be considered enormous.

Among the most ancient races, the Assyrians, Babylonians, Chaldeans, Phoenicians and Hebrews; in India, China, Persia, Egypt, Greece and Rome, in fact, among almost all cultural and primitive races, we find many customs and traditions associated with honey. These beliefs, closely connected and intimately interwoven with their domestic, social and religious lives, offer plentiful and intriguing material for research. On solemn occasions, like births, weddings, funeral services, and during religious ceremonies honey played an important rôle. Honey was considered a sacred substance, symbolizing the purest and noblest in Nature. It was looked upon not only as a food and medicine, but as a talisman, a protector from all evil. Among the Germanic and Slavic races there was a belief that if one ate honey on Maundy Thursday he would gain protection for the year against all diseases, and if honey were sprinkled in a room on Holy Saturday it would kill all vermin. In Poland and Silesia honey was given to the cows and even rubbed into their eyes to prevent pestilence. To ward off contamination of wells, honey was poured into them. A string dipped into honey at sunrise and tied around a fruit tree would produce a rich fruit crop. Blessing the fields with honey was an old pagan custom. The ancient Germanic farmer, after he had finished plowing the first furrow, poured milk and honey into it. This was called *Ackersegen*. The ritual was especially employed when there was a suspicion that the fields were blighted by magic.

Many beliefs and customs connected with honey existed among the populations of all countries. For example, stingy or quarrelsome people, it was believed, were never successful in producing honey. Every year, one had to send some honey and wax to the neighbors in appreciation of their courtesy in allowing the bees to feed on their flowers. Denying honey to the sick meant empty combs in the future. To refuse honey to children was a sin against Mary and Joseph, who had fed Child Christ. To send honey to a dying person, however, was bad luck. Selling honey was prohibited among many nations but barter was permitted. Menstruating women had to keep away from the hives, otherwise the honey would turn sour.

A tree in which wild bees had nested and stored their honey was reputed to possess occult powers. Girls would carry a splinter from such trees to entertainments to assure themselves of being well supplied with dancing partners. Farmers carried the branches with them when they drove their cattle to market, with the expectation of securing good buyers. The Slavs called a bee-tree a lucky tree, and a branch of it, broken off on St. Andrew's day, was considered a lucky charm. In Finland there is a belief that if a girl bakes a honey cake on Christmas Eve, keeps it in her bed overnight, and then gives a piece to her sweetheart, he will remain true to her through life. There was a widespread belief among many nations that where there were honey and bees, lightning would not strike and the devil would never approach.

In enumerating only a few of the superstitious beliefs,

customs and traditions connected with honey, the writer has
thought it best to group them according to the three paramount and most solemn events of life, namely, birth, marriage and death.

1. BIRTH

The use of honey was only rarely omitted during birth-
rites. Among Babylonians, Iranians, Egyptians and Hebrews,
honey and milk was the first nutriment which touched the
lips of a newborn. Calvin mentions in Isaiah, Ch. IX, that,
"the Jews to this day, give their infants a taste of honey and
butter before they suck." The Galician Jews put a piece of
honeycomb into the cradle before the infant is placed in it.
During Hindu birth ceremonies, after a male infant is born
and the umbilical cord is severed, the father touches the lips
of the son with honey taken from a golden vessel and applies
it with a golden spoon, at the same time giving the child its
name. The Hindus hang a branch of the sacred tree, smeared
with honey, over their doors with the invocation: "The young
child cries to it; the cow that has a young calf shall low to
it." Amongst the Mohammedans in the Province of Punjab
(N. W. India) the most respected member of the family puts
ghutti (made of honey) into the mouth of the infant as its
first food and holds honey over its head to ward off evil
spirits.

There were similar customs among the Greek, Roman,
Slavic and all Anglo-Saxon races. The Scotch Highlanders,
soon after the birth of a child, takes a fresh branch of ash
(melia, mel=honey) which secretes a sweet manna-like juice,
burn it at one end and after smearing some honey on the
other end, they daub with it the lips of the infant. The
Scotch believe that honey, being a sacred substance, should
be the first food to touch the palate of the new-born. An
identical ceremony prevails in Finland and in the Caucasus.
During birth ceremonies in modern Greece a chosen child
smears honey on the lips of the infant with the prayer: "Be
thou as sweet as this honey." To give honey to an infant as
its first food was also a heathen Germanic custom.

If honey were placed on the lips of an infant by some
miraculous means, it was believed that the act bestowed the
gift of poetic inspiration and eloquence or that the child
would become a saint. Cicero described how Plato, yet an
infant, was taken by his father to Mount Hymettus to offer

sacrifices to the Muses. The child was laid in a thicket and while he slept a swarm of bees built a honeycomb in his mouth which presaged the singular sweetness of his discourses and his future eloquence. The same miracle happened to Xenophon, Sophocles, Pindar, Virgil, Lucanus, St. Ambrose, St. John Chrysostomus, St. Dominic, St. Isidor and many others. Among the Mohammedans, there is a superstition that if one dreams of a bee he will become a great singer. The bee was a symbol of the Koran. In Hungary the population believed that when a son was born to the King, the bees put honey on his lips for good luck. Homer was nursed by priestesses whose breasts distilled honey. Zeus, the god of Mount Olympus, was nursed on honey. The Greeks and Teutons believed that honey conferred immortality.

(Thomas Huxley, the famous biologist, humorously referred in his biography to the magic power of honey to endow mellifluous eloquence. He deplored his lack of oratorical talent, because the power of speech gains higher places in Church and State than worth, ability or honest work. Huxley blamed his incompetency in this respect on a lamentable incident: "A neighboring beehive emitted a swarm and the new colony, pitching on the window sill, was making its way into the room when a horrified servant shut down the sash. If that well-meaning woman had sustained from her ill-timed interference the swarm might have settled on my lips and I should have been endowed with eloquence.")

Once honey had touched the lips of an infant, the act was supposed to confer on it a certain magic spell. According to the ancient laws of Friesland, a father was permitted to expose an infant to its doom, but after the child had tasted honey and milk its life had to be spared. Hieron II as an infant was exposed in the fields by his father Hierocles, because the child was born to him by one of his servants. The bees cared for the foundling and fed him on honey. When the father learned of the miracle his attitude toward his son changed. The child was raised with great solicitude and received a liberal education. Hieron subsequently became a noted patron of literature and chief of the army, and as such won the battle of Mylae (296 B.C.). After the victory he became king of Syracuse.

When the Pharaoh of Egypt gave the order that all male Hebrew children should be destroyed by drowning them in the Nile, Jewish mothers were constrained to give birth to their children in the fields. The mother of Moses kept the future Prophet concealed for three months, and it would not be surprising if he also were brought up on honey. This might account for his wisdom, eloquence and prophetic powers. According to the Biblical legend (Exod. R. 23: 8), the exposed children were given two pebbles, from one of which they obtained oil, and from the other, honey.

2. MARRIAGE

"Und süss wie der Honig
    Ist der Ehestand."
(And sweet as honey is wedlock.)

In nuptial ceremonies and in the matrimonial lives of most ancient nations and of many of the primitive races to this day, honey has played just as important a rôle as in birth-rites. In Egypt, honey was considered such an essential substance that in every marriage contract the bridegroom had to promise to supply his bride yearly with a definite amount of honey. When the nuptial knot was tied, the bridegroom said, "I take you for my wife and bind myself to furnish you annually with twenty-four hins (32 pounds) of honey" (Brugsh). During Hindu wedding ceremonies honey offering was an important function. The bridegroom kissed the bride and said: "This is honey, the speech of my tongue is honey, the honey of the bee is dwelling in my mouth and in my teeth dwells peace." During the course of the services the bride's forehead, mouth, eyelids, ears and genitals were anointed with honey. In Bengal, the Brahmans believed that if the bride's pudenda were covered with honey it would produce fertility. When the Dekan Hindu bridegroom called on the bride, honey and curds were offered to him with the object of scaring away evil spirits. The Hindu firmly believed that honey had the magic power to ward off demoniacal spirits, so much feared during marriage ceremonies.

We find similar customs among African natives. In Galla-land, a country bordering on Abyssinia, honey was an important food and a principal commodity of trade. Before a wedding the Galla bridegroom had to bring a fair quantity of honey to the intended bride. If the amount were unsatisfactory, the bride and her family rejected him as a future husband. The Galla women have the reputation of being the most independent among the women of Eastern Africa.

In Morocco, the wedding guests are offered honey before the ceremonies. During the nuptial rites no honey is used because it is reserved for the cult of the dead. After the wedding the groom feasts on honey to which also the Moroccans attribute a powerful aphrodisiac effect. The nuptial supper of a Roman couple consisted of milk, honey and poppy-juice.

On the European continent among the Greeks, Nordic, Germanic, and Slavic races honey had an important function before, during and after wedding festivities. The Poles sang a song at weddings: "Diligent is the life on a farm, like the life of the bee, and marriage is sweet as honey." When a Polish bride reached her home after the ceremonies, she was led three times around the fire-place, her feet were washed and when she entered the bridal chamber she was blindfolded and honey was rubbed on her lips. In Hungary the bride baked honey cake during full moon and gave it to the groom to secure his love. During the celebration of marriages the young couples were fed with honey by wise women. This was supposed to sweeten their wedded life. In Croatia the parents of the bridegroom await him at the threshold of the house with a pitcher of honey. The container must not be made of glass. When the groom appears he asks his mother what is in the pitcher. The answer is: "My son, it contains my honey and thy good will." When the bride enters the house she is offered by her mother-in-law a spoonful of honey. The spoon is several times withdrawn but finally with a sudden dash is put into her mouth. The bride is given, besides, a nosegay and a cup of honey. While the bride walks around the house she spreads honey over each threshold and door. In Dalmatia and Herzegovina there is the same custom; even the wedding ring is dipped into honey during the ceremonies. In Slovakia, milk and honey; in Silesia, cooked barley and honey; in Bulgaria, bread and honey are given to the bride. The Bulgarians offer a special soup to the bridal couple, called *okrap*, which is made from wine and honey. The wedding cake baked with honey is broken over the head of the bridegroom and some honey is rubbed on his face. The woman who anoints the groom exclaims: "Be fond of each other as the bees are fond of this honey." In Serbia, Albania, Rumania and Turkey similar customs prevail, especially among the gipsy tribes.

During Swedish wedding festivities honey was liberally

used. According to ancient records in 1500, when the daughter of a wealthy Swede, named Krogenose, was married, half a ton of honey was consumed. In 1567, during the wedding feast of Sigrid Sture, 453 jars of honey were used. The Finns also did justice to honey and, more so, to honey drinks.

In modern Greece some of the ancient customs still persist. When the bride arrives at the groom's cottage, his mother stands waiting at the door with a jar of honey of which the bride must partake that the words of her lips may become sweet as honey. The remaining contents of the jar are smeared in the lintel of the door, that strife may never enter the home. In Rhodes, when the groom arrives in his new home, he dips his finger into a cup of honey and traces a cross on the door.

In Brittany, Westphalia and Lincolnshire the betrothals are announced to the bees and the hives are decorated with red or white ribbons; part of the wedding cakes are placed before them and the new couples must introduce themselves to the bees, otherwise their married life would surely be unlucky.

In Hungary, where honey always was an important food, the production had fallen off considerably after the World War. The town of Kecskemét decided that every newly married couple should receive from the municipality a beehive and a swarm of bees as a wedding present to encourage apiculture. (If one—or both—of the contracting parties were stung, the city fathers may also be blamed for it.)

We could not very well close this chapter without reflecting on the meaning of a popularly used term, honeymoon.* Some philologists (probably with conjugal experiences) have suggested that this sweetest period of wedlock was compared with the moon because as soon as this celestial body reaches a full phase it commences to wane, not unlike the affection of wedded couples. Others have thought that the allusion stems from the ancient custom whereby the bride and groom were wont to eat honey and drink mead during the first four weeks of their married life. That a honeymoon is not necessarily "sweet" can be adjudged from Hood's poem:

---

* The era between the years 1898 to 1902 was called the *honeymoon period* of American industry. Collective bargaining was introduced and the accord between employers and employees was compared with the harmony of newlyweds.

"The moon, the moon, so silver and cold,
 Her fickle temper has often been told—
 Now shady—now bright and sunny;
 But of all the lunar things that change,
 The one that shows most fickle and strange,
 And takes the most eccentric range,
 Is the moon—so called—of honey!"

3. DEATH

Honey had a wider use and more significance during burial services and funeral rites than during ceremonies for either birth or marriage. Many ancient races, among them the Egyptians, believed that the souls of the departed continued to live and required food for their future maintenance, otherwise they would starve. According to ancient concept, the body was destroyed, but not the soul, which survived and was supposed to return to earth. Death was considered not so much the departure of the body but that of the soul, freed of its fetters, in flight to a future destination. Honey, as a rule, symbolized death among the ancients, an allusion to the sweetness of death, contrasted with the bitterness of life. The Greeks also thought that life was bitter and death sweet. Honey was offered to Hecate, the Chthonian Artemis. Hecate's by-name was Melitodes (honey-like).

There was no other more appropriate and favored food for the dead than honey. It was an established custom among the Hindus, Chinese, Babylonians, Egyptians, Greeks and Romans to place honey next to the corpse. Similar practices were in vogue among the ancient Mexicans, the North American Indians and the Eskimos. The Japanese supplied not only food and drink but also clothing for their dead.

Before burial, the so-called funeral repast was placed next to the bier and rations were also stored in the graves to supply the needs of the deceased. On solemn occasions, especially on death anniversaries, ritual services were held by relatives and friends during which the most favored provisions of the departed ones were laid on the burial places or in the tombs. Honey and wine were often sprinkled over the graves and over the funeral pyres.

In the various copies of the Egyptian *Book of the Dead* which are the most ancient scripts, originating as far back as the Pyramid Age, honey is often mentioned. In the tombs of kings, next to the mummies, jars of honey were placed. When found, this honey was still in a fairly good state of preservation. The great papyrus of Rameses III records that during his reign of thirty-one years, millions of jars of honey were purchased from the royal treasury for sacrificial offerings. There is an inscription on a tomb in the Necropolis of Abidos: "The King appoints that a sum of three and a half pounds of silver from the Treasury of the Temple of Osiris be given in order to cover the *daily* demand for one measure of honey, to be used at the ceremony of the worship of the dead, for his beloved Naromantha." The picture shows how the Royal Butler, accompanied by the sacred bull, carried honeycombs and lotus blooms to the tomb of the royal dead.

Honey sacrifices consisting of honey, honey cakes and edible plants were often tendered to the Egyptian gods. The lips of the priests were anointed with honey and part of the sacrificial food was later consumed by the believers (Plutarch, Op. Ch. 68).

During the funeral rites of many nations, the wish was expressed that the departed ones might find a land where there was plenty of honey. The Mohammedan dream was a land with rivers of honey; this was also Mohammed's promise to the faithful and his true conception of Paradise.

The Greeks and Romans excelled all other nations in bringing honey sacrifices to the graves. In the *Iliad* Achilles offers honey at the bier of his friend Patroclus, who was killed after he had driven back the Trojans.

> "And he sat therein two-handled jars of honey and oil,
>   Leaning them against the bier."

Achilles also sprinkled honey on the grave as an offering to the Chthonian gods.

Aeschylus describes in *The Persians* the honey libations which Queen Atossa tenders to her husband, Darius:

> "I return, and bear
> Libations soothing to the father's shade
> In the son's cause; delicious milk, that foams
> White from the sacred heifer; liquid honey,
> Extract of flow'rs."

Euripides pictures Iphigenia at the grave of her brother bringing honey sacrifices:

"For him, as dead, with pious care
This goblet I prepare;
And on the bosom of the earth shall flow
Streams from the heifer mountain-bred,
The grape's rich juice, and mix'd with these,
The labor of the yellow bees,
Libations soothing to the dead.
Give me the oblation: let me hold
The foaming goblet's hallowed gold."

In the *Odyssey*, Circe advises Ulysses upon entering Hades to sprinkle the shadows of the dead with honey, milk and wine. Hesiod's grave in Locris was deluged with honey by the pious shepherds. Zarathusthra paid homage in similar manner.

We learn from one of the dramas of Lucian, the celebrated Greek satirist, why honey was poured over the graves. Charon, the boatman of the underworld's black river, ascends to the world above and with the guidance of Hermes surveys the realm of mortals. The first thing he wishes to see is, of course, the places where the dead bodies are inhumed. The ferryman expresses his astonishment upon seeing there all the honey and mead, which mortals call libations, poured over the graves in honor of the dead.

Charon exclaims:

"Why, then, crown they
These stones, and why with unguent rich anoint them?
And why do some, heaping a funeral pile
Before the mounds, and digging out a trench,
Burn sumptuous viands there, and in the ditches
Pour, if I right conjecture, mead and wine?"

Hermes explains:

"I know not ferryman, what use it can be
To those in Hades; but it is believed
That souls returning from the world below
Will come to supper—very probable!
Hovering above the savor and the smoke,
And from the trench will drink up the metheglin."

Supplying the dead with food was originally a heathen custom which later became a Christian ritual. In Russia and many other countries, even today, a jar of honey is placed

next to the corpse and some is desposited in the grave. The
Russian *kutja* (death food) is made of flour, poppy seeds and
honey. Some of it is consumed by the funeral guests, the rest
left for the dead. Honey cake, as a sacrificial offering to the
deity, had an Indo-Germanic origin.

Among many African tribes, placing honey next to the bier
and in the grave, is still a custom. The Indians gave their
dead honey and rice.

Honey was considered by all ancients a sacred substance,
the purest and best thing in the world, the symbol of eternal
bliss. There was an old belief that if a corpse was preserved
in honey it would reincarnate. Democritus firmly believed
that. There are many mythical tales that people who perished
in honey revived. The ancients undoubtedly were impressed
with the efficiency of honey in protecting organic matter from
decay and the origin of the belief in the miraculous preserv-
ing power of honey can be ascribed to this appreciation.

Ancient cultural states and also primitive races used their
best efforts to preserve their dead and prevent decomposition
of the body. The simplest method was to expose the corpse
to the influence of the sun-rays until the body fluids evaporated and the tissues dried up. This is still practiced by some
savages.

The Egyptians, Babylonians, Persians, Assyrians and Arabs
used honey and wax for embalming their prominent dead.
Herodotus records that the Babylonians buried their dead in
honey. He also relates the same about the Assyrians, who,
however, first covered the corpses with wax. The old Spartan
Kings were embalmed in honey, as were Justinian, the Byzan-
tine emperor, and Alexander the Great. Alexander the Great,
as Statius records, ordered before his death that his remains
be preserved in honey. Aristotle, his teacher, had undoubtedly made him appreciate the conserving power of honey.
Aristotle wrote an extensive thesis on this phase of honey,
which however was lost in the conflagration of the library in
Alexandria. Strabo described, in his fourteenth book, how the
body of Alexander the Great was placed in a golden coffin
filled with white honey. Herod I, King of Judea (40–4 B.C.),
the superstitious despot and tyrant, more hated than any
other person of his age, in a fit of jealousy ordered his
beautiful wife, Marianne, to be executed; after which he kept
the dead body in honey for seven years—because, he
avowed, he loved her. Aristobulos, whom Caesar had ordered

to Syria and who was poisoned by the followers of Pompeius, was also embalmed in honey, until Anthony sent the remains to Judea to be entombed in the royal sepulchre. The Assyrians and Persians (Herodotus I. 198) covered corpses with wax and then buried them in honey. The dead body of Agesilaus was covered with wax, we learn from Plutarch. "The attendants of Agesilaus had no honey to preserve the body (he died in a foreign country), so they embalmed it with melted wax and thus carried it home." Cornelius Nepos and Plutarch ascribed the adoption of the use of wax to a scarcity of honey. Homer in the *Odyssey* (XXIV. 68) describes the funeral of Achilles, "buried in the garments of the gods and in sweet honey." The *Iliad* (XIX. 38 and XXIII. 170) also renders an account of how the dead were anointed with honey. An old Egyptian script mentions that a corpse in honey mummifies in 120 years.

The secret of the remarkable art of Egyptian embalming is entirely lost. This is not surprising because the mysterious process was unknown even to the contemporary Egyptians. The embalmers, as a rule, inherited the proficiency from their ancestors. All we know from the Greek and Roman writers of antiquity is that the contents of the cranial, pleural and abdominal cavities were removed and filled with aromatic herbs, fragrant spices, balsams, oil of cedar, etc. That the corpse afterwards was placed in honey or wrapped in honey-soaked bandages seems more than probable because several allusions in the Egyptian papyri intimate that honey converts a corpse into a mummy in the course of years. Columella repeatedly mentions the embalming of bodies in honey. The honey-loving philosopher Democritus was also preserved in honey. Abd' Allatif relates that some men, searching for treasures in the Egyptian tombs near the Pyramids, discovered a sealed cruse and upon opening it they found that it contained honey. They began to dip their bread into it when one of them noticed hairs upon his fingers. The jug was carefully examined and was found to enclose the body of a small child in a perfect state of preservation. After the body was entirely withdrawn, rich jewels and brilliant ornaments with which the child was covered, were revealed.

In Persia burial in honey also was practiced. In one of their manuscripts there is even a prescription for making mummies for profit. A red-haired man had to be fed until he reached the age of thirty. Then he was to be drowned in honey and drugs and the vessel sealed. After 150 years, according to the script, the honey transformed the corpse into a mummy. The reason for supplying mummies for commercial purposes was because powdered mummies were credited with curative value for both internal and external diseases. In the sixteenth and seventeenth centuries mummy-powder was in great demand and sold in the apothecaries for a good price. For this reason many tombs were plundered. The Jews in the East and the French were the best customers and used it for various maladies (Ambroise Paré). The powder had an aromatic sweet-acrid taste. It was used externally for wounds to prevent gangrene. The Arabs use it even today for the purpose. The belief in the Middle Ages in the curative effect of honey seems to suggest that the substance was used for embalming. There is a sepulchral inscription in Thelmessos (Greece), of the first century A.D.:

> "Here lies Boethos, Muse-bedewed, undying,
> Joy hath he of sweet sleep in honey lying."

In the famous medieval Romanesque cathedral of Bamberg, on the tomb of Henry II (Saint), Emperor of the Holy Roman Empire, who died in 1024, there is the following inscription:

> "Sus lit er da in sîner stift
> di'er het erb, awen, als diu bin ir wift
> ûz manege bluete wurket, daz man honc-seim nennet."

("He lies in the minster he built, as the bee her web from many a blossom works, which we name honey-juice.")

When King Edward I of England, who died in 1307, was exhumed in 1774, his hands and face were found to be well preserved. This condition was attributed to the fact that they had been coated with a thin layer of wax and honey.

In Burma, during the rainy season, the eviscerated corpses are preserved temporarily in honey, until relatives are able to procure dried fire-wood for the customary cremation. If the dead person buried in honey is a holy Buddhistic monk and the corpse is removed from the coffin for cremation, the honey is dispensed in one ounce jars and sold at auction. Often fortunes are realized from such sales. The Burmese firmly believes that a drop of this honey will cure any affliction.

*   *   *

The ancient belief that anyone who drowned in honey would revive, is best illustrated in the legend of Glaucos.

Glaucos, the son of the Cretan King Minos, while playing with a mouse (the symbol of death) fell into a jar of honey and drowned. Minos searched for him in vain. At last he appealed to the oracle of Apollo and only under its guidance did he find the body of his son. Apollo announced to Minos: "A monstrosity has been born in your land and the person who will be able to discover its meaning shall *find* and *restore* your son." The whole country looked for the monstrosity, which was very soon found. It proved to be a calf which changed its color thrice daily; first it was white, then it became red and finally black. Minos summoned all his augurs to find out what this signified. The seer Polydos was the one who could construe its meaning. He thought the calf represented a mulberry tree, the fruit of which is first white, afterwards red and when ripe, black. Minos ordered Polydos to find his son. At first he hesitated but after he was compelled, he commenced his search for the lost son of the King. Polydos, during his long wanderings, passed a honeybin, on top of which an owl was perched, driving away some bees. He considered this an omen, entered the bin and found Glaucos, drowned in a vessel of honey.

Polydos notified the King of the recovery of Glaucos' body. The seer was locked in a vault with the corpse and ordered to resuscitate it. A snake soon crawled toward the body of Glaucos, but Polydos killed the snake. Another snake, bearing an herb, laid this over the dead snake, which at once revived. Polydos then placed the same herb over the body of Glaucos, who immediately came to life. Polydos received royal rewards for his deeds and was discharged, laden with treasures.

The circumstance that the bees which tried to enter the honeybin were driven away by the owl, was symbolical of the fact that the bees, representing the soul of the deceased, were using their best efforts to regain their former habitation and were prevented only by the sinister influence of the owl.

CHAPTER XIX

HONEY IN POETRY, SYMBOLISM, EXPRESSIONS AND NAMES

Honey is frequently mentioned in the works of all poets and writers, especially by the oriental and classical writers. Honey represented to them all things that are sweet and pleasing to the palate, to the mind and to the heart. Honey, like the bees, was a symbol of spirituality and also of poetic inspiration; it was looked upon as psychic nourishment—the food of the saints, carried by the bees even to the thrones of the gods. Metaphorical references to honey are found in innumerable phrases, names, proverbs, and symbols; to all intents and purposes alluding to its many noteworthy characteristics. Honey and the hive shared in popularity. Honey and the sting of the bee were often contrasted.

Bees were called by the Greeks and Romans the *Birds of the Muses*. The golden bees were supposed to have gathered honey for the poets on thyme-covered Mount Hymettus to sweeten their verses.

Hindu poetry is literally drenched in honey. Madhukara (honeyborn) had three meanings: bee, lover and moon. There are many romantic Hindu tales associated with honey.

In the *Rig-Veda*:

> "My tongue hath honey at the tip, and sweetest honey at the root.
> Thou yieldest to my wish and will, and shalt be mine and only mine.
> My coming in is honey sweet, and honey sweet my going forth;

> My voice and words are sweet: I fain would be like honey in
>   my look
> Around thee have I girt a zone of sugar-cane to banish hate
> That thou may'st be in love with me, my darling, never to
>   depart."

In Hindu mythology all delightful endowments were symbolized by honey. When *mem-sahib* (woman) was forged by Twasktrie, the Hindu Vulcan, he mixed a little honey in the raw material. The ingredients, by the way, were the following: The buoyancy of the leaves, the velvety gloss of the fawn, the brilliancy of the sun's rays, the tears of the mist, the inconstancy of the winds, the trepidation of the hare, the vanity of the peacock, the softness of the dawn on the throat of the swallow, the hardness of the diamond, *the sweetness of honey*, the cruelty of the tiger, the warmth of fire, the chill of snow, the chatter of the jay, and the cooing of the dove. From these components he created Woman and presented her to man. (Evidently, with a bountiful spirit of giving "something to remember me by.")

According to the Greek and Roman literature, honey possessed the magic power to confer the genius of poetry and eloquence; in Hindu mythology, even wisdom.

The deep influence which honey always has had on mankind is demonstrated by the innumerable geographic designations which include the name honey. In India, Egypt, the Holy Land; Greece, Italy, and in fact, on the entire European Continent and in Africa there are many names of towns, mountains, lakes and rivers which are associated with the word honey.

In Greece there are several towns called Melita or Melite. The classical name of the Island of Malta was Melita (Sicilian spelling). Melville, means honey-town; Melrose, honey-rose. In Germany, Austria, Hungary and the Slavic countries we find innumerable names derived from bees and honey. Dardanos, a village near the Strait of Dardanelles, means bee-town (darda in Turkish, bee).

In England there are Honington (honey farm) in Suffolk; Honeydon in Bedfordshire; Honnington and Honiley in Warwickshire; Honeybourne and Honeybrook in Worcestershire. There are several Clonmels (honey-meadow) in Ireland.

In the United States:

Honey, Mississippi	Honeycreek, Iowa
Honey, North Carolina	Honey Creek, Oregon
Honey Hill, South Carolina	Honeycreek, Wisconsin
Honey Bend, Illinois	Honeyford, North Dakota
Honey Creek, Illinois	Honeygrove, Texas
Honeybrook, Pennsylvania	Honey Island, Louisiana
Honeygrove, Pennsylvania	Honey Lake, California
Honeycreek, Indiana	Honeyville, Oklahoma

The word amber also seems to be associated with honey. It was believed that amber was anointed with honey (ambrosia). Amber is an old English name for pitcher. Amberstone and Honeycrock in Sussex are adjoining. In Wiltshire there are Ambresbury and Mount Ambrosius. The name Melleray (Brittany), a town where the Trappist monks established an abbey, was derived from mellearium (apiary). The good old Irish name Mahoney is probably a contraction of the words my honey.

Melos (song), Melpomene, melodrama, melody, melon, mellow (rich in flavor), mellifluous, mellify, etc., etc., are derived from the root, mel=honey. "My honey" is a favorite expression of the Southern negro. In old Latin writings, we also find *puella mellita* (honey girl). *Honey boy* is a recent acquisition. The verb *honey* means to flatter, cajole.

The expression *sardonic laugh* also originated from honey. On the Island of Sardinia, there is a plant from which honey is collected by the bees and if this is consumed it will cause a grim, convulsive, often fatal laugh.

*   *   *

There are many legendary myths and fairy tales which glorify the bees, not only for industry, economy and the political perfection of their state but especially for supplying mankind with heaven-born honey. James Northcote's fable, *The Bee and the Ant*, is a typical illustration. "Violent dispute once arose between the Bee and the Ant, each claiming superiority for prudence and industry; and, as neither of them would give up the point, they agreed to refer the decision of the great question to the decree of Apollo, who was fortunately at hand tending the cattel of Admetus. Accordingly, approaching the god, each made out his title to preference, with all the eloquence of which a Bee or an Ant had ever been master. Then Apollo gave judgment thus: 'I consider you both as most excellent examples of industry and prudence.' 'You', said he, addressing the Ant, 'by your care, your foresight and your labor, make yourself ample provision in time of need; thus independent, you never intrude on or tax the labors of others for help; but recollect, at the same time, that it is yourself alone that you benefit; no other creature ever shares any part of your hoarded riches. Whereas the Bee practices, by his meritorious and ingenious exertions, that which becomes *a blessing to the world*. Therefore I must give judgment in favor of the Bee."

MISCELLANEOUS PROVERBS

Honey sometimes turns sour. (The end of good luck.)

The diligence of the hive produces the wealth of honey.

A drop of honey will not sweeten the ocean.

Don't have honey watched by a bear (make a goat the gardener).

If you want to gather honey, don't kick over the beehive. (Abraham Lincoln.)

Honey young, wine old.

Every bee's honey is sweet.

Honey you swallow, gall you spit.

If you are too sweet, the bees will eat you.

Make honey out of yourself and the flies will devour you (Cervantes—*Don Quixote*. II. 43.)

Where there is honey, the bears come uninvited.

The bear dreams of honey.

To your own honey the devil puts one spoon; to strange honeys, two spoons.

Luxury has honey in her mouth, gall in her heart, and sting in her tail.

Where bees are, there is honey.

Where a bee sucks honey, the spider sucks poison.

A still bee gathers no honey. Old bees yield no honey. Dead bee maketh no honey.

No bees, no honey; no work, no money.

Who is afraid of the sting never earns honey.

If you love honey, don't fear the sting.

Honey is not far from the sting.

Who collects honey and roses must bear the stings and the thorns.

Wit is honey lent, without the sting. (Tennyson.)

The following are some of the many foreign sayings and proverbs associated with honey:

LATIN

Where there is honey, there are bees. (Ubi mel, ibi apes.) Plautus.

Deadly poisons are concealed under sweet honey. (Impia sub dulci melle venena latent.) (Ovid—Amorum I. 8.)

Where honey, there is gall. (Ubi mel, ibi fel.) This was, by the way, the favorite saying of Martin Luther.

Honey in mouth, sting in tail. (In ore mel, in caude aculeum habet.)

GERMAN

Who shares honey with a bear, gets the least of it.

Honey is not meant for an ass.

Honey is too good for the bear.

Honey is sweet, but the bee stings.

Bees have honey in their mouths, but stings in their tails.

Bees bring honey, honey brings bees.

FRENCH

A drop of honey catches more flies than a barrel of vinegar.

A little gall spoils a great deal of honey.

A honey tongue and a heart of gall. (Bouche de miel, coeur de fiel.)

Who deals with honey will sometimes be licking his fingers.

Who has no honey in his pot—let him have it in his mouth.

It is dearly bought honey, that is licked off a thorn. (Cher est le miel qu'on lêche sur epines.)

SPANISH

Michael, Michael, you have no bees and yet you sell honey.

ITALIAN

Rub yourself with honey and the flies will eat you. (Fatevi miele, che le mosche vi mangieramo.)

RUSSIAN

If you make a honey barrel out of yourself, everybody wants
to eat you.

ARABIAN

Honey in the hive of good fortune quickly sours.
A lazy man is never fed on honey.
Lick up the honey and ask no questions.

CHINESE

Bees make honey and men eat it.
When the nest is destroyed others get the honey.

PERSIAN

Honey is a wonderful substance but it does not help the
dead. (Sadi.)

INDEX

Acacia honey, 48, 145
Achard, Franz, 25
Ackersegen, 181
Adulterated honey, 42–43
Aelian, 99
Aeneid, 103, 138
Aeschylus, 188
Aesculapius, 103
Africa, 71, 103, 104, 157, 165, 184, 190
Alergoba honey, 48
Alfalfa honey, 17, 20, 43, 44, 49
Alkalinity of honey, 22–23
Allen, John Taylor, 155
Amber, 196
Ambrosia, 137, 171
Ameiss, F. C., Dr., 117
American Bee Journal, 124
American Honey Institute, 53
American honeys, 16–17, 20–21, 41, 43–47
Anacreon, 7, 173
Analyses of honey, 17, 20–21, 23
Anderson, John, 12
Anemia, 22
Annals of Internal Medicine, 110
Anti-hemorrhage value of honey, 21–22
Antiquities of the Jews (Josephus), 167
Antiseptic, honey as an, 97, 123–127
Aphrodisiac, honey as an, 4–5, 13, 99–100, 104, 185
Apis dorsata (giant bee of India), 137
Apis indica (hive-bee of India and China), 137

Apollonius, 7, 70
Apple honey, 17
Arabia, 38, 96, 97, 99
Aristotle, 70, 169, 190
Aristoxenus, 99
Ash tree, 172
Assyrians, 4, 97, 134, 180
Athenæus, 7
Athol porridge (mead of Scotland), 76
Athole brose, 75
Aughinbaugh, W. E., Dr., 125
Austria, 93, 144, 145
Aztecs, 147

Babylonians, 4, 72, 134, 180
Backlava (recipe), 62
Bacteria destroyed by honey, 23–24, 123
Banting, F. G., Dr., 27
Barberini manuscript, 166
Basswood honey, 47
Bee and the Ant, The (Northcote), 196–197
Bee designs on ancient monuments, 135
"Bee line," 84, 156
Bee smoker, 87, 89
Bee stings, 80, 88–89, 106, 116, 117
Bee suit, 87, 88
Bee veil, 87
"Bee woman," 159–161
Beehive, construction of, 85
Beehives, 4, 141, 165; tax on, 144
Beekeepers, 4, 9, 10, 11, 12, 13, 90–93
Beekeeper's symbol, 157

201

KITCHEN POWER!

☐ AMERICA'S FAVORITE RECIPES FROM BETTER HOMES & GARDENS
(NE4578 • 95¢)
☐ THE ART OF BARBECUE & OUTDOOR COOKING—Tested Recipes
(NE4782 • 95¢)
☐ THE ART OF FISH COOKING—Milo Milorandovich (SE4832 • 75¢)
☐ THE ART OF FRENCH COOKING—Fernande Garvin (PE5225 • $1.00)
☐ THE ART OF GERMAN COOKING—Betty Wason (NE4309 • 95¢)
☐ THE ART OF ITALIAN COOKING—Mario LoPinto (NE6668 • 95¢)
☐ THE ART OF JEWISH COOKING—Jennie Grossinger (QE4703 • $1.25)
☐ THE ART OF SALAD MAKING—Carol Truax (PE5936 • $1.00)
☐ THE ART OF VIENNESE COOKING—Marcia Coleman Morton
(SE4888 • 75¢)
☐ BETTER HOMES & GARDENS CASSEROLE COOKBOOK (NE4633 • 95¢)
☐ THE COMPLETE BOOK OF MEXICAN COOKING—Elizabeth Ortiz
(NE4107 • 95¢)
☐ THE COMPLETE BOOK OF PASTA—Jack Denton Scott (NE5347 • 95¢)
☐ THE COMPLETE BOOK OF VEGETABLE COOKERY—Myra Waldo
(SE4791 • 75¢)
☐ THE COMPLETE BOOK OF WINE COOKERY—Myra Waldo
(NE6672 • 95¢)
☐ FANNIE FARMER BOSTON COOKING SCHOOL COOKBOOK—Wilma Perkins
(QE5324 • $1.25)
☐ FANNIE FARMER JR. COOKBOOK—Wilma Perkins (SE4677 • 75¢)
☐ THE HAWAII COOKBOOK & BACKYARD LUAU—Elizabeth Toupin
(SE5724 • 75¢)
☐ THE HERB AND SPICE BOOK—Craig Claiborne (NE5427 • 95¢)
☐ HORS D'OEUVRE CANAPES—James Beard (SE4384 • 75¢)
☐ ORIENTAL COOKING—Myra Waldo (SE5222 • 75¢)
☐ PANCAKE COOKBOOK—Myra Waldo (SE4665 • 75¢)
☐ THE RUSSIAN COOKBOOK—Barbara Norman (NE5233 • 95¢)
☐ THE SPANISH COOKBOOK—Barbara Norman (NE5852 • 95¢)
☐ TUESDAY SOUL FOOD COOKBOOK (SE4708 • 75¢)
☐ YOGA NATURAL FOODS COOKBOOK—Richard Hittleman
(PE5765 • $1.00)

Buy them wherever Bantam Bestsellers are sold or use this handy coupon:

Bantam Books, Inc., Dept. KP, Room 2450, 666 Fifth Ave., N.Y., N.Y. 10019

Please send me the titles checked above. I am enclosing $_____
(Check or money order—no currency or C.O.D.'s, please. If less than 5
books, add 10¢ per book for postage and handling.)

NAME_____

ADDRESS_____

CITY_____STATE_____ZIP_____

Please allow about four weeks for delivery.   KP 5/71

JOHN NAYLOR

presents

YOUR LUCKY STARS

Day-by-day Astrology Forecasts

Noted author and President of the British Federation of Astrologers John Naylor reveals everything you always wanted to know . . . about YOU. Find out what's "in the stars"—from his detailed daily predictions on health, romance, career, money, marriage, travel and everything that matters to you. These compact guides for each sign of the zodiac are indispensable aids for everyone who wants to be prepared for the future— and the present. Get your own sign—as well as those for the people you love.

March 1971 to September 1971 Forecasts

____FX6161	ARIES	____FX6167	LIBRA
____FX6162	TAURUS	____FX6168	SCORPIO
____FX6163	GEMINI	____FX6169	SAGITTARIUS
____FX6164	CANCER	____FX6170	CAPRICORN
____FX6165	LEO	____FX6171	AQUARIUS
____FX6166	VIRGO	____FX6172	PISCES

Just 50¢ each!